USA Word Search for Kids Ages 8-10

Wizo Learning

FREE BONUS

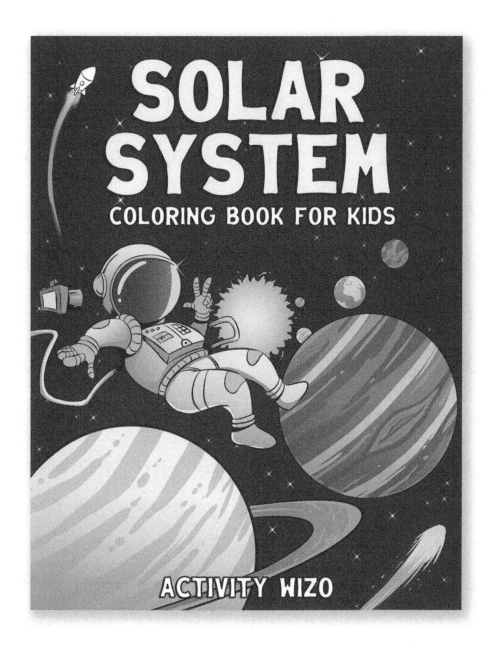

Just flip to the end of the book
to get the link!

ALABAMA CITIES

```
X  L  X  G  Z  Z  L  D  Y  F
M  A  D  I  S  O  N  A  G  V
H  U  N  T  S  V  I  L  L  E
O  K  Z  I  V  L  H  E  G  U
O  D  O  T  H  A  N  V  S  F
V  L  R  Y  K  I  G  I  D  A
E  B  O  M  O  B  I  L  E  U
R  A  U  B  U  R  N  L  O  L
D  E  C  A  T  U  R  E  I  A
M  O  N  T  G  O  M  E  R  Y
```

- **Montgomery** is the capital city of the state
- **Auburn** is the largest city in eastern Alabama
- **Daleville** is also called Gateway to Fort Rucker
- **Decatur** is located near the Tennessee River
- **Dothan** is known for processing peanuts
- **Eufaula** is the largest city in Barbour County
- **Hoover** is home to the Riverchase Galleria
- **Huntsville** is known for cotton textile mills
- **Madison** is known for its high-quality schools
- **Mobile** has the Alabama's only saltwater port

ALABAMA LANDMARKS

```
U  W  M  F  B  Y  U  C  H  I
E  I  R  O  A  P  E  R  R  F
Y  L  L  I  R  X  H  N  E  O
S  S  D  D  T  G  X  W  D  E
L  O  E  R  O  G  A  Y  S  B
O  N  X  Y  N  L  C  N  T  F
S  A  T  U  R  N  T  C  O  F
S  U  E  Q  E  D  M  U  N  D
X  E  R  Q  S  C  D  C  E  Q
T  A  N  N  E  H  I  L  L  L
```

- **Barton** Hall is called Cunningham Plantation
- **Dexter** Avenue Baptist Church, Montgomery
- **Edmund** Pettus Bridge was declared in 2013
- **Morgan** Fort is located at mouth of Mobile Bay
- **Redstone** Test Stand was used to test missile
- **Saturn** V dynamic test stand is a rocket tester
- **Sloss** Furnaces operated for iron production
- **Tannehill** Ironworks is in Tuscaloosa County
- **Wilson** Dam is named after a US President
- **Yuchi** Town is a historic archaeological site

ALASKA CITIES

```
S N F W A S I L L A
E K A P B E T H E L
L E I E E Q X G I Q
D T R V A L D E Z Q
O C B R O D I G G S
V H A Y S L M C S C
I I N T J U N E A U
A K K L A W O C K N
O A S T T K S H V D
X N H Y D A B U R G
```

- **Juneau** is the capital city of the state
- **Bethel** is the main port of Kuskokwim River
- **Fairbanks** is home to the University of Alaska
- **Hydaburg** was formed in 1911 from villages
- **Ketchikan** has most number of totem poles
- **Klawock** has the oldest hatchery in Alaska
- **Pelican** was developed in the late 1930s
- **Seldovia** has been home to commercial fishing
- **Valdez** is home to radio broadcaster KCHU
- **Wasilla** is named after Chief Wasilla

ALASKA LANDMARKS

```
F  Q  B  S  I  T  K  A  B  G
Z  V  R  Z  A  X  X  X  I  W
A  W  O  L  D  V  X  Z  R  A
N  G  O  B  I  H  O  Y  N  L
A  S  K  A  G  W  A  Y  I  E
N  P  S  Q  E  L  P  L  R  S
G  C  H  A  L  U  K  A  K  I
U  P  O  R  T  H  O  D  O  X
L  M  D  X  X  V  R  D  H  L
A  N  E  N  E  N  A  H  S  F
```

- **Anangula** site is an archaeological site
- **Birnirk** has sixteen prehistoric mounds
- **Brooks** River has an Archaeological District
- **Chaluka** Site has a large midden
- **Ladd** Field is the US military Airfield
- SS **Nenana** is a steam-powered boat
- Holy Assumption **Orthodox** is an old church
- Old **Sitka** Site was declared in 1962
- **Skagway** Historic District has old buildings
- **Wales** has artifacts from the Birnirk culture

ARIZONA CITIES

```
M  H  C  Y  S  E  D  O  N  A
T  E  T  U  C  S  O  N  Q  F
R  O  S  M  O  S  X  A  E  P
X  V  M  A  T  Y  K  K  D  R
E  W  J  B  T  E  M  P  E  E
F  L  A  G  S  T  A  F  F  S
S  U  D  J  D  T  V  S  L  C
H  F  X  J  A  G  O  U  I  O
F  C  C  J  L  K  Z  N  T  T
E  P  H  O  E  N  I  X  E  T
```

- **Phoenix** is the capital city of the state
- **Flagstaff** is called the city of seven wonders
- **Mesa** is known for its beautiful mountains
- **Prescott** was the capital of Arizona until 1867
- **Scottsdale** is known for fine resorts and spas
- **Sedona** is known for majestic red rock scenery
- **Tempe** is home to state's juried arts festivals
- **Tombstone** is a historic city in Cochise County
- **Tucson** was developed by European Americans
- **Yuma** is noted for its weather extremes

ARIZONA LANDMARKS

```
A  H  U  A  C  H  U  C  A  W
U  K  H  B  G  S  F  J  H  F
J  L  O  W  E  L  L  E  X  P
B  V  V  S  I  E  R  R  A  U
W  E  G  I  N  M  B  O  H  E
I  N  A  K  I  V  L  M  X  B
H  T  T  H  U  B  B  E  L  L
T  A  L  I  E  S  I  N  K  O
V  N  I  K  T  W  C  A  S  A
N  A  N  X  Y  L  C  V  Y  N
```

- **Casa** Malpaís was declared in 1964
- **Gatlin** Site belongs to the town of Gila Bend
- Fort **Huachuca** is a US Army installation
- **Hubbell** Trading Post lies on Highway 191
- **Jerome** Historic District was declared in 1966
- **Lowell** Observatory is made by Percival Lowell
- **Pueblo** Grande Ruin and Irrigation Sites
- **Sierra** Bonita Ranch is a very old cattle ranch
- **Taliesin** West was home to a famous architect
- **Ventana** Cave is an archaeological site

ARKANSAS CITIES

```
S G K C O N W A Y A
P E H X G B S A M H
R N E I M K H O A O
I T P H Y W E K U X
N R Q I M D R Y M I
G Y F Z G L W B E E
D P A R A G O U L D
A J O H N S O N L X
L F N N H T D T E A
E G P R E S C O T T
```

- **Springdale** is known for meat processing
- **Conway** is a well-known center of education
- **Gentry**, known for a 400-acre animal safari
- **Hoxie** is a small city in Lawrence County
- **Johnson** is a city confronting population boom
- **Maumelle** has extensive bicycle trail systems
- **Paragould** has a humid subtropical climate
- **Piggott** is a lovely city in Clay County
- **Prescott** had its telephone system by 1890
- **Sherwood** experiences all four seasons

ARKANSAS LANDMARKS

```
T  O  L  T  E  C  V  Q  Y  D
B  H  I  E  R  E  G  P  I  A
A  N  Q  C  O  N  A  T  Y  I
T  A  O  E  H  T  J  K  V  S
H  Q  P  D  W  E  J  F  E  Y
H  Q  A  M  E  N  A  R  D  R
O  P  R  E  R  N  D  S  D  D
U  H  K  W  K  I  A  L  D  K
S  Q  I  E  C  A  M  D  E  N
E  V  N  I  R  L  M  N  H  F
```

- **Bathhouse** Row is a collection of bathhouses
- **Camden** Expedition Sites has 9 historic places
- **Centennial** Baptist Church is a historic church
- **Daisy** Bates House is located in Little Rock
- **Eaker** Site lies on Eaker Air Force Base
- **Menard** Hodges is an archaeological site
- **Nodena** Site was a 15-acre palisaded village
- **Parkin** Indian Mound was declared in 1964
- **Rohwer** War Center was declared in 1992
- **Toltec** Mounds is an archaeological site

CALIFORNIA CITIES

```
H O C E A N S I D E
A B O A K L A N D F
Y X K F F K C I H O
W T T A R W R H P N
A Y H S E E A Q O T
R R M B S X M O M A
D W W Q N I E O O N
N I E L O P N I N A
S M O D E S T O A T
S T O C K T O N T N
```

- **Sacramento** is the capital city of the state
- **Fontana** remained rural until World War II
- **Fremont** is noted as site of the Tesla Factory
- **Fresno** is known for fruits and vegetables
- **Hayward** is named after William Hayward
- **Modesto** is located near Stanislaus River
- **Oakland** is known for 155-acre Lake Merritt
- **Oceanside** is a coastal city on South Coast
- **Pamona** was Queen of the Citrus Belt in 1920s
- **Stockton** seaport is gateway to Central Valley

CALIFORNIA LANDMARKS

```
G A K D O N N E R B
I L P A R S O N S C
J C W Z B C F B G A
B A L B O A E W U R
U T M V E S Y O A R
B R A D B U R Y J I
R A C A R M E L O Z
V Z B K S U R U M O
L C H I C A N O E G
V M E N D O C I N O
```

- **Alcatraz** Island lies in San Francisco Bay
- **Balboa** Park is a historic urban cultural park
- **Bradbury** Building is an architectural landmark
- **Carmel** Mission Basilica Museum
- **Carrizo** Plain is known as the Place of Rabbits
- **Chicano** Park is famous for its outdoor murals
- **Donner** Memorial Park is site of Donner Camp
- **Guajome** house is a historic house museum
- **Mendocino** Woodlands Park, a camping spot
- **Parsons** Memorial Lodge was built in 1915

COLORADO CITIES

```
Z  T  H  O  R  N  T  O  N  R
A  L  H  V  S  A  L  I  D  A
T  Y  B  N  S  O  I  N  F  Q
A  S  P  E  N  Y  T  W  E  U
D  B  R  I  G  H  T  O  N  Z
E  L  G  R  E  E  L  E  Y  Y
N  A  D  Q  D  Y  E  Z  R  R
V  M  T  C  O  R  T  E  Z  J
E  A  Z  C  L  W  O  E  G  Q
R  R  D  U  R  A  N  G  O  H
```

- **Denver** is the capital and most populous city
- **Aspen**, known for its luxurious real estate
- **Cortez** has great archaeological resources
- **Brighton** is named after Brighton Beach
- **Greeley** is home to Union Colony Civic Center
- **Durango** is famous for narrow gauge railroad
- **Lamar** has a number of historical attractions
- **Littleton** is part of Front Range Urban Corridor
- **Salida** is known as the crossroads
- **Thornton**, easternmost city in northern Denver

COLORADO LANDMARKS

```
F  L  E  A  D  V  I  L  L  E
L  S  L  C  U  Q  S  D  T  Z
A  I  U  T  R  J  A  K  J  Q
G  L  U  R  A  I  P  H  C  U
S  V  E  U  N  Q  P  S  L  P
T  E  K  J  G  R  H  P  J  I
A  R  J  I  O  I  I  I  L  K
F  T  E  L  L  U  R  I  D  E
F  O  P  L  Q  M  E  I  Y  S
H  N  L  O  V  E  L  A  N  D
```

- **Cripple** Creek District is known for gold mining
- **Durango** & Silverton Narrow Gauge Railroad
- **Flagstaff** Mountain lies in Boulder County
- **Leadville** District was designated in 1961
- Downtown **Loveland** Historic District
- **Pikes** Peak is named after an American explorer
- **Sapphire** lies in the heart of Rocky Mountains
- **Silverton** Historic District is known for mining
- **Telluride** Historic District was founded in 1878
- **Trujillo** Homestead is a historic ranch site

CONNECTICUT CITIES

```
A  D  A  N  B  U  R  Y  G  G
N  N  O  I  L  T  K  F  R  R
O  O  S  S  H  E  L  T  O  N
R  R  I  O  G  L  N  J  T  O
W  W  T  M  N  V  F  N  O  X
I  A  M  E  R  I  D  E  N  B
C  L  U  Z  Y  E  A  M  K  I
H  K  H  A  R  T  F  O  R  D
W  A  T  E  R  B  U  R  Y  C
T  O  R  R  I  N  G  T  O  N
```

- **Hartford** is the capital city of the state
- **Ansonia** is also called the Copper City
- **Danbury** is nicknamed as the Hat City
- **Groton** is the Submarine Capital of the World
- **Meriden** became famous as the Silver City
- **Norwalk** is a unique coastal destination
- **Norwich** is known as the Rose of New England
- **Shelton** survived major arson fires in history
- **Torrington** was originally called Wolcottville
- **Waterbury** is home to Post University

CONNECTICUT LANDMARKS

```
F R E D E R I C F C
N U G V Z X B Z U O
E G R O V E I A Q M
W K I M B E R L Y P
G R S T F O D B A O
A M W W A Y C I L U
T J O A O A R I E N
E Q L I L R A V L C
F N D N B N F Q I E
Q G I L L E T T E T
```

- **Birdcraft** Sanctuary is the oldest in US
- Lake **Compounce** is an amusement park
- **Frederic** Remington House is a historic house
- **Gillette** Castle State Park attracts tourists
- Florence **Griswold** Museum is an art museum
- **Grove** Street Cemetery lies in New Haven City
- **Kimberly** Mansion is a historic house
- Old **Newgate** Prison is a former prison
- Mark **Twain** House is a Museum in Hartford
- **Yale** Bowl Stadium, a college football stadium

DELAWARE CITIES

```
P  S  I  N  Q  D  Z  H  S  W
L  E  W  E  S  E  D  A  C  I
R  A  A  W  Q  L  J  R  Q  L
E  F  K  A  U  A  Z  R  M  M
H  O  H  R  Y  W  T  I  I  I
O  R  M  K  F  A  P  N  L  N
B  D  O  V  E  R  X  G  F  G
O  D  V  S  C  E  J  T  O  T
T  T  T  A  B  R  T  O  R  O
H  C  A  S  T  L  E  N  D  N
```

- **Dover** is the capital city of the state
- New **Castle** is situated on Delaware River
- **Delaware** City is located in New Castle County
- **Harrington** is known for harness racing
- **Lewes** is an incorporated city on Delaware Bay
- **Milford** is home to 15 MW, 80 acre Solar Farm
- **Newark** is the safest city in Delaware state
- **Rehoboth** Beach is a city on the Atlantic Ocean
- **Seaford** hosted Eastern Shore Baseball League
- **Wilmington** is the largest city of the state

DELAWARE LANDMARKS

```
H  G  R  P  S  P  U  H  Z  H
O  P  B  V  T  X  T  D  M  A
W  N  E  M  O  U  R  S  C  G
A  S  P  E  N  D  A  L  E  L
R  Z  Z  C  U  N  A  T  Y  E
D  N  L  O  M  B  A  R  D  Y
R  S  E  R  K  A  L  M  A  R
I  V  M  B  E  R  Z  C  T  E
C  H  R  I  S  T  I  N  A  L
W  I  N  T  E  R  T  H  U  R
```

- **Aspendale,** a historic house declared in 1970
- Fort **Christina** was named after Queen Christina
- **Corbit** Sharp House is a historic house museum
- **Hagley** Museum and Library covers 235 acres
- **Howard** High School of Technology
- **Kalmar** Nyckel is a replica of a Swedish ship
- **Lombardy** Hall is a historic house in Fairfax
- **Nemours** Mansion is a 300-acre estate
- **Stonum** is a historic house declared in 1973
- **Winterthur** Museum, Garden and Library

FLORIDA CITIES

```
S  L  P  O  J  M  I  A  M  I
S  Z  E  F  X  X  X  E  Q  C
S  A  N  I  B  E  L  N  Z  L
H  U  S  Y  H  X  G  P  E  E
I  L  A  K  E  L  A  N  D  R
A  F  C  Z  K  T  D  K  B  M
L  V  O  O  R  L  A  N  D  O
E  C  L  J  C  B  F  M  M  N
A  U  A  C  V  O  A  X  P  T
H  A  P  O  P  K  A  G  S  A
```

- **Miami** is the financial center of Florida
- **Apopka** had the US longest serving mayor
- **Clermont** is home to 1,956 Florida Citrus Tower
- **Cocoa**, founded before the civil war by settlers
- **Hialeah** has a large Spanish-speaking communit
- **Lakeland** is home to Circle B Bar Reserve
- **Orlando** is famous for Disney World
- **Pensacola** is also called the city of five flags
- **Sanibel** is a popular tourist destination island
- **Tampa** is economic center of western Florida

FLORIDA LANDMARKS 18

```
V  Q  Q  X  P  F  L  S  T  C
I  W  M  I  H  L  L  C  U  A
Z  I  G  H  Q  A  A  S  Y  S
C  N  X  Y  E  G  M  Z  H  T
A  D  M  J  L  L  B  H  A  I
Y  O  D  A  D  E  I  U  X  L
A  V  S  R  N  R  A  I  T  L
J  E  F  F  E  R  S  O  N  O
U  R  A  I  L  R  O  A  D  U
V  E  N  E  T  I  A  N  A  L
```

- **Castillo** de San Marcos is a masonry fort
- **Dade** Battlefield is located in Sumter County
- **Flagler** House is named after Henry M. Flagler
- **Jefferson** County Courthouse is in Monticello
- **Llambias** House was designated in 1970
- **Plaza** Ferdinand VII lies in Pensacola Village
- South Florida **Railroad** is a historic railroad
- **Venetian** Waterway Park is a concrete trail
- **Vizcaya** Museum and Gardens is in Miami
- **Windover** Archeological Site covers 1.3 acres

GEORGIA CITIES 19

```
H C O L U M B U S B
I S R O S W E L L R
N M A C X V F D N O
E I V V D P C G E O
S L X J A D F E W K
V T L M J N W I N H
I O A T L A N T A A
L N P T T M C A N V
L A T H E N S V H E
E D U N W O O D Y N
```

- **Atlanta** is the capital and most populous city
- **Athens** is home to the University of Georgia
- **Brookhaven** was approved in a referendum
- **Columbus**, site of the final Civil War battle
- **Dunwoody** was officially incorporated in 2008
- **Hinesville** is home to the Fort Stewart
- **Milton** is named after War hero John Milton
- **Newnan** is also called the City of Homes
- **Roswell** is a city named after Roswell King
- **Savannah** is the oldest city of Georgia

GEORGIA LANDMARKS

U	A	M	I	C	A	L	O	L	A
F	M	A	U	H	P	Y	C	E	K
O	A	R	E	I	O	S	T	U	O
L	R	S	B	P	O	Q	A	H	L
K	I	H	A	P	P	V	G	A	O
S	E	A	B	E	Q	W	O	R	M
T	T	L	P	W	J	Z	N	D	O
O	T	L	T	A	M	P	A	M	K
N	A	N	D	A	Y	V	V	A	I
R	I	V	E	R	F	R	O	N	T

- **Amicalola** Falls State Park is on 829-acres
- **Chippewa** Square, known for the battle in 1812
- **Folkston** Railfan Platform was built in 2001
- **Hardman** Farm covers a 173-acre area
- **Kolomoki** Mounds is one of the largest in the US
- **Marietta** Cemetery was founded in 1866
- **Octagon** House is also known as May's Folly
- **Riverfront** Plaza is Situated in Savannah
- **Tampa** Riverwalk is a pedestrian trail
- **Marshall** Forest is located in Floyd County

HAWAII CITIES ㉑

```
P W A I L U K U G A
U A M E L G S X G H
K I H O N O L U L U
A P K G V U M A A I
L A X S U N A O H M
A H Y W K R K I A A
N U T W T I A N I N
I K A N E O H E N U
R T H W H I A E A J
Q N K A P O L E I T
```

- **Honolulu** is the state's capital and largest city
- **Ahuimanu** lies on the island of Oahu
- **Kaneohe** has the ancient Hawaiian fishponds
- **Kapolei** takes its name from the volcanic cone
- **Kihei** features 6 miles of beautiful beaches
- **Lahaina** is the tropical gateway in Hawaii
- **Makaha** Beach has the best surfing on Oahu
- **Pukalani** is also known as Window of Heaven
- **Wailuku** is the gateway to lush Iao Valley
- **Waipahu** is the name of an artesian spring

HAWAII LANDMARKS

```
P W H E E L E R C X
H H T F L L J K W Z
I O L A N I U A I G
C N L A H A I N A B
K O I I R M I E A S
A K F K A U N O L U
M O X A T L W H O W
G H U T N L C E H N
K A L A U P A P A F
R U M O O K I N I N
```

- **Aloha** Tower is a retired lighthouse
- **Hickam** Air Force Base was built in 1938
- **Honokōhau** Settlement lies in Kona District
- **Iolani** Palace was the royal residence
- **Kalaupapa** National Historical Park
- **Kaneohe** Bay is the Marine Corps Air Station
- **Kaunolū** Village Site covers a 640-acre area
- **Lahaina** Historic District was declared in 1962
- **Mookini** Heiau is in remote North Kohala
- **Wheeler** Army Airfield is located in Honolulu

IDAHO CITIES (23)

```
E  F  A  P  R  B  H  P  J  H
C  A  L  D  W  E  L  L  V  A
C  R  A  T  H  D  R  U  M  Y
H  S  R  B  N  X  R  T  J  D
U  N  D  M  O  C  K  M  B  E
B  A  M  E  R  I  D  I  A  N
B  M  L  E  W  I  S  T  O  N
U  P  O  R  A  F  O  E  G  H
C  A  P  L  U  M  M  E  R  E
K  R  O  B  E  R  T  S  G  Y
```

- **Boise** is state's capital and most populous city
- **Caldwell** is part of Boise Metropolitan Area
- **Chubbuck** is named after a railroad conductor
- Headquarters of Empire Airline in **Hayden**
- **Lewiston** is famous as Idaho's hottest city
- **Meridian** is among US fastest growing cities
- **Nampa** is known for quality food processing
- **Plummer** has the humid continental climate
- **Rathdrum** is close to tons of beautiful lakes
- **Roberts** is a small city in Jefferson County

IDAHO LANDMARKS

```
I  N  M  H  E  L  E  M  H  I
N  F  W  A  L  L  A  C  E  Y
X  C  Z  W  G  W  S  K  P  F
L  W  B  K  Z  U  S  O  C  H
Y  B  P  B  V  C  A  M  A  S
K  O  A  I  N  B  Y  W  T  E
T  I  G  L  A  L  A  W  A  G
K  S  U  L  M  B  O  P  L  J
W  E  I  P  P  E  T  L  D  I
K  C  B  Z  A  D  I  M  O  E
```

- **Assay** Office is a historic building in Boise
- **Boise** Depot is a former train station
- **Camas** Meadows Battle Sites, declared in 1877
- **Cataldo** Mission is a heritage-oriented park
- USS **Hawkbill** (SSN-666) was a submarine
- **Lemhi** Pass is a high mountain pass
- **Lolo** Pass, highest point of historic Lolo Trail
- **Nampa** Historic District was registered in 1983
- **Wallace** Historic District is in Shoshone County
- **Weippe** Prairie is known for Camas flowers

ILLINOIS CITIES

```
A  P  H  K  E  C  A  S  E  Y
U  R  S  J  L  H  W  U  W  C
R  I  W  O  G  P  J  Z  J  H
O  R  P  L  I  V  M  Z  D  I
R  A  B  I  N  G  D  O  N  C
A  L  Q  E  E  R  P  C  H  A
R  T  Y  T  V  L  K  I  B  G
R  O  C  K  F  O  R  D  Y  O
G  N  O  F  C  A  N  T  O  N
C  B  E  L  V  I  D  E  R  E
```

- **Springfield** is the capital city of the state
- **Abingdon** is a beautiful city in Knox County
- **Alton** has the limestone bluffs along the river
- **Aurora** is known as the City of Lights
- **Belvidere** is called the City of Murals
- **Canton** was founded by a settler, Isaac Swan
- **Casey** is known for Guinness World Records
- **Chicago** is famous for interesting architectures
- **Elgin** was known as Butter Capital of the World
- **Joliet** is known for the Des Plaines River

ILLINOIS LANDMARKS

```
R  M  B  J  W  K  R  D  Y  N
K  O  L  P  O  E  V  K  W  A
I  R  E  U  Y  N  C  T  U  U
N  R  L  B  R  N  A  D  X  V
C  O  H  Y  U  I  H  T  R  O
A  W  L  I  N  C  O  L  N  O
I  W  R  R  O  O  K  E  R  Y
D  F  Q  Q  W  T  I  D  Q  Z
M  O  D  O  C  T  A  Y  E  N
B  G  R  O  S  S  E  P  S  N
```

- **Cahokia** Mounds was designated in 1982
- **Grosse** Point Light is a historic light house
- **Kennicott** Grove has John Kennicott's house
- **Kincaid** Site is an archaeological Site
- **Lincoln** Tomb is Abraham Lincoln's tomb
- **Modoc** Rock Shelter lies in Randolph County
- **Morrow** Plots, experimental agricultural field
- **Nauvoo** Historic District was built in 1839
- Sears, **Roebuck** and Company Complex
- **Rookery** Building is a historic office building

INDIANA CITIES

```
L  A  F  A  Y  E  T  T  E  G
I  H  S  G  O  S  H  E  N  R
L  A  W  R  E  N  C  E  J  E
P  M  P  C  H  O  E  D  T  E
O  M  Z  A  A  M  H  P  C  N
R  O  S  H  W  R  T  E  H  F
T  N  S  D  R  P  M  G  L  I
A  D  M  U  N  C  I  E  S  E
G  F  I  S  H  E  R  S  L  L
E  E  B  K  O  K  O  M  O  D
```

- **Carmel** is famous for highly educated people
- **Fishers** transitioned from town to city in 2015
- **Goshen** is noted for recreational vehicles
- **Greenfield**, birthplace of the Hoosier dialect
- **Hammond** is known for famous Lake Michigan
- **Kokomo** opened world's first McDonald's Diner
- **Lafayette** is named after a French general
- **Lawrence** is a beautiful city in Marion County
- **Muncie** became industrial center after 1880s
- **Portage** is known as a heavily industrial city

INDIANA LANDMARKS

```
G R O T T O X O U M
R V C O R Y D O N A
O J Z L A U L H P D
U M H A Q Z E C A I
S I X N D P V L Y S
E L V I F R I E Z O
L L B E N J A M I N
A E B R P J T E X B
N R Y Z A M C N S O
D C A N N E L T O N
```

- **Benjamin** Harrison Home was built in 1870
- **Cannelton** Cotton Mill was declared in 1991
- **Clement** Studebaker House lies in South Bend
- **Corydon** Historic District has historic buildings
- **Grotto** of Our Lady of Lourdes, Notre Dame
- **Grouseland** was William Harrison's residence
- **Lanier** Mansion is a historic house in Madison
- **Levi** Coffin House is located in Fountain City
- **Madison** Historic District was declared in 2006
- **Miller** House was designed by Eero Saarinen

IOWA CITIES

```
I N D I A N O L A N
W C C D U B U Q U E
N A D R A L B I A W
E X T R E M O J D T
D A V E N P O R T O
P Z T B R X N M A N
B V G T X L E L M V
J O H N S T O N E G
M I Z P I K E O S I
D M A D R I D X I K
```

- **Albia** is a small city in Monroe County
- **Ames** is home to Iowa State University
- **Boone** is a city located in Des Moines Township
- **Davenport** is located on the Mississippi River
- **Dubuque** is locally known as Tri-State Area
- **Indianola** was incorporated in 1863
- **Johnston** was named after railway supervisor
- **Madrid** is known for coal mining
- **Newton** is home to Iowa Speedway Farm
- **Waterloo** was called Prairie Rapids Crossing

IOWA LANDMARKS

```
T E R R A C E J D N
S E Q I K E Q G U H
E W C P L F M A B R
R O P Y H F L S U K
G O J U L I E N Q I
E D G H K G P U U M
A B B I E Y R P E B
N U I J R N Z R S A
T R F S D V Z P V L
C Y H E R B E R T L
```

- **Abbie** Gardner's Cabin lies in Arnolds Park
- **Dubuque** County Jail is a historic building
- **Effigy** Mounds National Monument
- **Herbert** Hoover Historic Site is at 186.8 acres
- **Julien** Dubuque's Mines is a state park
- **Kimball** Village is an archaeological site
- **Phipps** Site was declared in 1964
- **Sergeant** Floyd is a historic museum boat
- **Terrace** Hill is also known as Hubbell Mansion
- **Woodbury** County Courthouse is in Sioux City

KANSAS CITIES

```
K  A  B  D  E  R  B  Y  T  J
H  U  T  C  H  I  N  S  O  N
A  K  K  S  O  T  R  A  P  X
Y  I  S  A  Q  O  R  O  E  L
S  Z  L  L  I  M  U  E  K  E
V  E  W  I  C  H  I  T  A  N
I  T  H  N  V  N  G  W  J  E
L  L  E  A  W  O  O  D  O  X
L  R  H  E  M  P  O  R  I  A
E  C  O  N  C  O  R  D  I  A
```

- **Topeka** is the capital city of the state
- **Concordia** is located on the Republican River
- **Derby** is known for its senior center
- **Emporia** was site for observing Veterans Day
- **Haysville** is known as Peach Capital of Kansas
- **Hutchinson** was called Salt City after 1887
- **Leawood** is known as the safest city in Kansas
- **Lenexa** is popular as the City of Festivals
- **Salina** is known as a trading center for wheat
- **Wichita** is the birthplace of Pizza Hut chain

KANSAS LANDMARKS

```
M  W  H  I  T  E  F  O  R  D
L  A  R  N  E  D  O  Q  R  X
K  H  R  Y  C  B  T  Q  I  P
E  S  H  A  W  N  E  E  Z  A
M  U  C  W  A  C  Z  N  G  R
A  O  B  U  G  K  O  P  S  K
R  C  N  N  O  R  M  A  N  E
A  I  J  R  N  S  H  W  A  R
I  N  I  C  O  D  E  M  U  S
S  H  A  S  K  E  L  L  T  R
```

- **Haskell** Institute was founded in 1884
- Fort **Larned** is located in Pawnee County
- **Marais** des Cygnes Massacre Memorial Park
- **Monroe** Elementary School is in Topeka
- **Nicodemus** Historic Site covers 161 acres
- **Norman** No. 1 Oil Well Site was drilled in 1892
- **Parker** Carousel is located in Abilene
- **Shawnee** Methodist Mission was built in 1830
- **Wagon** Bed Spring is also called Lower Spring
- **Whiteford** (Price) Site is an archeological site

KENTUCKY CITIES

```
I  I  R  V  I  N  E  Y  L  O
N  M  F  C  J  A  G  C  F  F
W  S  R  R  U  S  S  E  L  L
G  I  A  K  L  H  Z  I  F  O
R  N  N  B  D  L  B  N  I  R
A  P  K  G  V  A  S  E  N  E
Y  Y  F  Q  O  N  L  Z  T  N
S  D  O  M  W  D  V  T  P  C
O  R  R  W  I  L  M  O  R  E
N  S  T  U  R  G  I  S  S  P
```

- **Frankfort** is the capital city of the state
- **Ashland** is an important economic center
- **Florence** area was known as Crossroads
- **Grayson** is a small city in Carter County
- **Inez** is home to several industrial employers
- **Irvine** is located on the Kentucky River
- **Russell** is the gateway to Lake Cumberland
- **Sturgis** was named after Samuel Sturgis
- **Wilmore** was crucial shipping point for cattle
- **Wingo** was established in 1854 as a stop

KENTUCKY LANDMARKS

```
C  K  Z  A  C  H  A  R  Y  E  E
H  M  O  R  R  I  S  O  N  P
U  A  T  L  M  P  L  T  D  H
R  M  W  E  N  D  O  V  E  R
C  M  I  L  M  V  C  K  D  A
H  O  T  P  D  I  U  O  F  I
I  T  T  I  S  J  S  J  U  M
L  H  A  N  Q  K  T  X  U  T
L  I  B  E  R  T  Y  C  P  C
P  E  R  R  Y  V  I  L  L  E
```

- **Churchill** Downs is a horse racing complex
- Dr. **Ephraim** McDowell House is in Louisville
- **Liberty** Hall is a historic house museum
- Historic **Locust** Grove is a 55-acre farm site
- **Mammoth** Cave National Park
- Old **Morrison,** Transylvania College
- **Perryville** Battlefield State Historic Site
- **Pine** Mountain Settlement School is in Bledsoe
- **Wendover** is also known as the Big House
- **Zachary** Taylor House is also called Springfield

LOUISIANA CITIES

```
J  M  O  N  R  O  E  S  K  P
E  A  B  F  H  Q  T  H  E  K
N  R  A  B  A  K  E  R  Y  A
N  K  S  U  Y  D  G  E  I  P
I  S  T  F  H  E  P  V  Q  L
N  V  R  Y  O  A  Q  E  P  A
G  I  O  A  U  C  Q  P  Q  N
S  L  P  P  M  X  O  O  H  O
A  L  E  X  A  N  D  R  I  A
K  E  N  N  E  R  Y  T  T  U
```

- **Alexandria** lies on south bank of Red River
- **Baker** is known for Baker Buffalo Festival
- **Houma** is famous for its Cajun food
- **Jennings** is called the Cradle of Louisiana Oil
- **Kaplan** is known for its rich music tradition
- **Kenner** is popular for its veteran population
- **Bastrop** was formally incorporated in 1857
- **Marksville** is named after Marc Eliche
- **Monroe** has a humid subtropical climate
- **Shreveport** Aquarium has 3000 plus animals

LOUISIANA LANDMARKS

```
G C J W P Y F F A P
C A H E T T Z L C L
P B L S S D U O A A
O I V L W U T C D Q
N L L Y I J P U I U
T D O L O E B S A E
A O N C M D R T N M
L P G A R D E N S I
B L U J A C K S O N
A K E A S E T O R E
```

- **Acadian** House was declared in 1974
- **Cabildo** is the Louisiana State Museum
- **Gallier** Hall, historic building in New Orleans
- **Garden** District started developing in 1832
- Fort **Jackson** is a historic masonry fort
- Fort **Jesup** was built in 1822 on 21-acre area
- **Locust** Grove Plantation lies in St. Francisville
- **Longue** Vue is a historic house museum
- **Plaquemine** Historic District has 133 buildings
- **Pontalba** Buildings were built in late 1840s

MAINE CITIES

```
I  R  A  C  A  R  I  B  O  U
H  W  B  U  U  B  D  D  Y  B
A  E  S  V  G  J  A  J  G  I
L  S  S  R  B  U  N  T  G  D
L  T  J  B  R  S  S  V  H  D
O  B  D  C  E  T  A  T  Q  E
W  R  I  J  W  X  C  C  A  F
E  O  H  U  E  Q  O  T  R  O
L  O  G  A  R  D  I  N  E  R
L  K  W  S  A  N  F  O  R  D
```

- **Augusta** is the capital city of the state
- **Bath** is commonly known as the City of Ships
- **Biddeford** is a beautiful city in York County
- **Brewer** was famous for bricks in 19th century
- **Caribou** is world's largest potato shipping hub
- **Gardiner** is famous for its old architecture
- **Hallowell,** small city in Kennebec County
- **Saco** became popular for its textile industry
- **Sanford** is known for its historic buildings
- **Westbrook** was originally called Saccarappa

MAINE LANDMARKS

M	C	I	N	T	I	R	E	V	K
C	X	K	E	N	T	R	Q	C	E
U	Y	P	W	P	A	T	H	S	N
S	J	E	E	Q	D	A	A	H	N
H	A	R	R	I	E	T	L	A	E
N	D	K	Q	J	X	E	I	F	B
O	H	I	N	D	W	E	F	U	E
C	G	N	K	O	Y	T	A	Q	C
D	H	S	I	A	X	H	X	T	R
B	H	A	R	P	S	W	E	L	L

- **Cushnoc** Archeological Site lies in Augusta
- Fort **Halifax** is a former British colonial outpost
- **Harpswell** Meetinghouse was declared in 1968
- **Harriet** Beecher Stowe House is in Brunswick
- **Kennebec** Arsenal is a historic arsenal
- Fort **Kent** is a Maine state park
- Fort **Knox** lies on the bank of Penobscot River
- **McIntire** Garrison House is a historic house
- **Perkins** Homestead is also called Brick House
- **Tate** House is a historic house museum

MARYLAND CITIES 39

```
F R U I T L A N D G
F B A L T I M O R E
R O N L A U R E L K
E F N C S L B D U O
D T A N E Y T O W N
E X P J P M O U N T
R R O C K V I L L E
I V L U J V I N L E
C R I S F I E L D M
K D S R H B O W I E
```

- **Annapolis** is the capital city of the state
- **Baltimore** is world famous for its crab houses
- **Bowie** has a large number of museums
- **Crisfield** is famous for its seafood
- **Frederick** is known for its civil war history
- **Fruitland** has a history as a port
- **Laurel** lies on the banks of Patuxent River
- **Rockville** was known as Hungerford's Tavern
- **Taneytown** is known for its history museum
- **Mount** Rainier lies in Prince George's County

MARYLAND LANDMARKS

```
D W Y E Y U W G A S
P X B L K Y X E I I
O B O L L M A N D O
H Z N I E D G A R N
A G T C R O W W P Y
M U N O M D U D K B
M O N T P E L I E R
O A N T I E T A M I
N K J G B P A D R C
D Q G T T U L I P E
```

- **Antietam** National Battlefield is on 3,230 acres
- **Bollman** Truss Railroad Bridge is in Savage
- **Brice** House was declared in 1970
- **Edgar** Allan Poe House and Museum
- **Ellicott** City Station was built in 1830
- **Hammond** Harwood House is historic museum
- **Montpelier** Mansion was declared in 1970
- **Sion** Hill is located in Havre de Grace city
- **Tulip** Hill is a plantation house
- **Wye** House was built between 1781–1784

MASSACHUSETTS CITIES

```
M  E  D  F  O  R  D  F  A  Y
W  X  L  M  B  M  B  R  C  V
O  B  N  V  E  E  C  A  H  H
R  V  J  K  V  L  E  M  E  O
C  H  A  V  E  R  H  I  L  L
E  Q  Y  T  R  O  T  N  S  Y
S  O  I  A  L  S  M  G  E  O
T  P  K  K  Y  E  I  H  A  K
E  B  O  S  T  O  N  A  V  F
R  Q  U  I  N  C  Y  M  R  S
```

- **Boston** is the capital city of the state
- **Beverly** is known for its industrial revolution
- **Framingham,** center of Metrowest region
- **Haverhill** was called the Queen Slipper City
- **Holyoke** is the Birthplace of Volleyball
- **Medford** was a leader in Clipper Ship building
- **Melrose** was first settled in 1628
- **Chelsea** is the smallest city in the state
- **Quincy** is known as the City of Presidents
- **Worcester** is called Heart of Commonwealth

MASSACHUSETTS LANDMARKS

```
G  R  G  O  D  D  A  R  D  V
R  B  E  A  U  P  O  R  T  E
O  W  A  Z  G  L  B  C  B  T
P  N  N  W  E  Y  O  W  R  E
I  F  U  L  L  M  A  M  A  R
U  E  S  D  M  O  R  Y  N  A
S  N  S  T  W  U  D  J  T  N
S  W  S  X  O  T  M  A  W  S
K  A  T  M  O  H  A  W  K  F
F  Y  Z  R  D  E  N  W  P  Z
```

- **Beauport** is also called Sleeper-McCann House
- **Boardman** House was built in 1692
- **Brant** Point Light is a lighthouse in Nantucket
- **Elmwood** was built in Georgian style
- **Fenway** Park is a baseball park in Boston
- **Goddard** Rocket Launching Site
- **Gropius** House is a historic house museum
- **Mohawk** Trail lies near the Greenfield city
- **Plymouth** Rock, traditional site in Plymouth
- **Veterans** Park is a city park in Holyoke

MICHIGAN CITIES

```
A  B  R  O  N  S  O  N  B  D
K  A  L  A  M  A  Z  O  O  E
A  A  H  D  W  B  U  R  C  A
D  B  A  L  L  D  F  B  L  R
E  M  R  T  A  F  R  W  A  B
T  T  R  U  P  N  A  T  W  O
R  E  I  S  E  M  S  J  S  R
O  S  S  Q  E  W  E  I  O  N
I  J  O  L  R  X  R  W  N  Q
T  Q  N  B  E  L  D  I  N  G
```

- **Lansing** is the capital of the state
- **Belding** was known as the Hog Wallow
- **Clawson** was incorporated in 1940
- **Dearborn** is the birthplace of Henry Ford
- **Detroit** is known for US automobile Industry
- **Fraser** is part of Metro Detroit region
- **Harrison** is named after a US President
- **Kalamazoo** is home to WMU University
- **Lapeer** is in southern Michigan on Flint River
- **Bronson** is located in central Branch County

MICHIGAN LANDMARKS

```
M  A  T  T  H  A  E  I  M  Z
B  C  R  A  N  B  R  O  O  K
C  E  D  I  S  O  N  H  T  U
A  P  A  B  R  I  E  I  O  W
L  E  V  V  B  I  S  G  W  T
U  W  J  J  B  U  T  H  N  S
M  A  R  S  H  A  L  L  I  E
E  B  G  Q  V  W  G  A  Y  Z
T  I  M  A  C  K  I  N  A  C
W  C  D  I  Q  J  Q  D  C  T
```

- **Calumet** Historic District was declared in 1989
- **Cranbrook** Educational Community
- **Edison** Institute is a large history museum
- **Ernest** Hemingway Cottage is in Petoskey
- **Highland** Park Ford Plant was built in 1910
- **Mackinac** Island is an island and resort area
- **Marshall** Historic District was settled in 1831
- **Matthaei** Botanical Gardens covers 300 acres
- **Motown** Museum is called the Hitsville U.S.A.
- **Pewabic** Pottery is a ceramic studio and school

MINNESOTA CITIES

```
M  R  P  L  Y  M  O  U  T  H
E  S  A  R  T  E  L  L  M  R
I  W  O  O  D  B  U  R  Y  O
P  A  N  C  M  E  D  W  I  S
B  U  J  H  B  D  U  L  Q  E
L  A  K  E  V  I  L  L  E  V
A  T  C  S  G  N  U  J  F  I
I  D  V  T  H  A  T  P  K  L
N  W  E  E  A  L  H  R  I  L
E  R  D  R  E  A  G  A  N  E
```

- **Rochester** has an extensive park system
- **Blaine** has the largest amateur sports facility
- **Duluth** is known for its Aerial Lift Bridge
- **Eagan** was settled as an Irish farming community
- **Edina** has nice parks and recreational facilities
- **Lakeville** is the largest city in Dakota County
- **Plymouth** has a humid continental climate
- **Roseville** has a mixed community land use
- **Sartell** straddles both sides of Mississippi River
- **Woodbury** is home to MSA Academy

MINNESOTA LANDMARKS

```
S  S  S  O  U  D  A  N  E  D
M  P  I  L  L  S  B  U  R  Y
A  U  Q  N  Y  D  Q  V  L  W
Y  Z  N  H  C  K  I  H  C  A
O  S  N  E  L  L  I  N  G  S
R  A  B  I  D  E  A  U  H  H
U  C  P  Z  O  K  B  I  C  B
K  E  L  L  O  G  G  W  R  U
J  Z  E  K  A  T  H  I  O  R
M  T  H  O  R  S  T  E  I  N
```

- **Kathio** Site is a Minnesota state park
- Frank B. **Kellogg** House is a historic house
- **Mayo** Clinic Buildings were listed in 1969
- **Pillsbury** A-Mill is a former flour mill
- **Rabideau** CCC Camp covers 18.8 acres
- **Sinclair** Lewis Boyhood Home is a museum
- Fort **Snelling** was completed in 1825
- **Soudan** Underground Mine State Park
- **Thorstein** Veblen Farmstead is in Rice County
- **Washburn** "A" Mill was rebuilt as a museum

MISSISSIPPI CITIES

H	B	C	S	T	F	I	L	P	G
T	B	W	O	A	U	T	B	E	U
U	I	U	U	H	S	P	L	A	L
U	L	U	T	H	E	A	E	R	F
L	O	Z	H	Q	K	W	Y	L	P
A	X	J	A	C	K	S	O	N	O
U	I	M	V	F	Q	I	F	B	R
R	U	L	E	L	A	N	D	J	T
E	O	B	N	M	O	R	T	O	N
L	R	I	D	G	E	L	A	N	D

- **Jackson** is the capital city of the state
- **Biloxi** is popular for its beaches
- **Gulfport** has become a tourism destination
- **Laurel** has Mississippi's oldest art museum
- **Leland** was long a center of cotton culture
- **Morton** is known for chicken processing plants
- **Pearl** is situated on the east side of Pearl River
- **Ridgeland** has the headquarters of Bomgar
- **Southaven** is childhood home of John Grisham
- **Tupelo** was incorporated in 1866

MISSISSIPPI LANDMARKS

```
L O N G W O O D L W
O D E N T Z E L W I
B U W C J Q J R A N
E N Y H U F O O V D
A L M E L R O S E S
U E W S G Z N A R O
V I P T S O E L L R
O T T E Q W I I E D
I H B R F W E E Y D
R M M O N M O U T H
```

- **Beauvoir** estate was built in Biloxi in 1848
- Highland Park **Dentzel** Carousel
- **Dunleith** is an antebellum mansion in Natchez
- **Hester** Site is a major archaeological site
- **Longwood** is also known as Nutt's Folly
- **Melrose** is a 15,000 square feet mansion
- **Monmouth** is a historic antebellum home
- **Rosalie** Mansion is a pre-Civil War mansion
- **Waverley** was formerly a plantation house
- **Windsor** Ruins are in Claiborne County

MISSOURI CITIES

```
F  P  L  I  B  E  R  T  Y  W
L  Q  J  O  P  L  I  N  B  B
O  I  X  G  U  B  Q  R  E  B
R  N  I  X  A  G  J  A  L  E
I  K  O  F  B  J  I  Y  T  U
S  L  I  X  T  U  D  T  O  R
S  G  L  A  D  S  T  O  N  E
A  M  O  N  E  T  T  W  E  K
N  O  G  Q  K  X  L  N  V  A
T  C  W  I  L  D  W  O  O  D
```

- **Belton** is a city in northwestern Cass County
- **Eureka** is called Gateway to Missouri Ozarks
- **Florissant** is home to Northwest HealthCare
- **Gladstone** is a beautiful city in Clay County
- **Joplin** is known for lead and zinc mining
- **Liberty** is home to William Jewell College
- **Monett** relies on manufacturing for economy
- **Nixa** was first settled by the farmers
- **Raytown**, a reminder of the sitcom Mama's Fami
- **Wildwood** is the home of the Al Foster Trail

MISSOURI LANDMARKS

```
R  F  G  A  T  E  W  A  Y  M
O  B  O  T  A  N  I  C  A  L
H  S  P  D  B  X  C  S  W  A
L  P  A  Q  D  V  U  O  A  N
R  Q  F  G  H  M  C  N  T  H
P  E  S  Z  E  C  T  J  K  E
S  A  N  B  O  R  N  H  I  U
J  D  T  J  O  P  L  I  N  S
C  S  Z  E  H  O  Z  U  S  E
G  O  L  D  E  N  R  O  D  R
```

- **Anheuser** Busch Brewery was opened in 1852
- Missouri **Botanical** Garden is in St. Louis
- **EADS** Bridge is both road and a railway bridge
- **Gateway** Arch is a 630 feet monument
- **Goldenrod** was designated in 1967
- Scott **Joplin** House State Historic Site
- Fort **Osage** was built in 1808 in Sibley village
- **Patee** House is known as Patee House Museum
- **Sanborn** Field, agricultural experiment field
- **Watkins** Mill is located in Lawson

MONTANA CITIES 51

```
F  C  H  B  H  E  G  Q  B  P
V  E  O  E  L  C  S  O  O  L
X  N  M  L  L  M  Z  C  Z  E
R  E  I  G  S  E  S  H  E  N
O  P  S  R  P  T  N  S  M  T
N  O  S  A  O  F  R  A  A  Y
A  P  O  D  X  F  Z  I  N  W
N  L  U  E  H  O  O  O  P  O
K  A  L  I  S  P  E  L  L  O
W  R  A  S  I  D  N  E  Y  D
```

- **Helena** is the capital city of the state
- **Belgrade** is under the Mayor-Council system
- **Bozeman** is called the most livable place
- **Colstrip** is the Energy Capital of Montana
- **Kalispell** is home to Glacier National Park
- **Missoula** is known for blue-ribbon trout fishing
- **Plentywood** is center for pulse crops purchase
- **Poplar** has a semi-arid climate
- **Ronan** lies on Flathead Indian Reservation
- **Sidney** relies heavily on farming and ranching

MONTANA LANDMARKS

```
T  R  A  V  E  L  E  R  S  R
S  O  J  N  Q  U  P  P  U  O
P  T  B  B  E  N  T  O  N  S
O  R  A  N  K  I  N  R  K  E
M  Q  N  D  H  J  F  T  N  B
P  E  N  Z  Z  A  T  A  X  U
E  F  A  Y  W  R  G  G  U  D
Y  B  C  Z  C  F  B  E  H  G
S  K  K  B  U  R  T  O  N  B
P  I  C  T  O  G  R  A  P  H
```

- **Bannack** is ghost town in Beaverhead County
- Fort **Benton** Historic District covers 20.2 acres
- **Burton** K. Wheeler House is a historic house
- **Hagen** Site is archaeological site near Glendive
- **Pictograph** Cave is an area of three caves
- **Pompeys** Pillar National Monument
- Great Falls **Portage** was designated in 1966
- **Rankin** Ranch is a historic ranch built in 1923
- **Rosebud** Battlefield State Park has 4220 acres
- **Travelers** Rest was built in 1805

NEBRASKA CITIES

```
Q I C B V X N X J X
U G V L I N C O L N
S E W A R D R P B L
N C G I J K A T E K
O L E R A L L M A E
R W N A E E S R T A
F R E M O N T N R R
O D V S W Z O F I N
L S A B Q U N M C E
K M J O M A H A E Y
```

- **Lincoln** is the capital city of the state
- **Beatrice** is located on the Big Blue River
- **Blair** is situated in the Loess Hills
- **Fremont** is home to Midland University
- **Geneva** is named after Geneva in Switzerland
- **Kearney** is home to several museums
- **Norfolk** is the birthplace of Thurl Ravenscroft
- **Omaha** has one of the world's best zoos
- **Ralston** is known for the Ralston Arena
- **Seward** is known for Fourth of July celebration

NEBRASKA LANDMARKS

```
C  A  C  W  A  L  K  E  R  Q
H  T  R  O  B  I  D  O  U  X
I  K  C  O  U  F  A  L  R  C
M  I  C  D  Z  Z  D  H  O  D
N  N  Q  Q  H  W  Q  A  B  A
E  S  C  H  U  L  T  Z  I  E
Y  O  Z  P  X  E  Z  A  N  C
B  N  J  I  G  A  O  R  S  M
P  A  L  M  E  R  Y  D  O  I
H  H  R  E  S  Y  W  D  N  A
```

- Fort **Atkinson** was 154.36 acre US Army post
- **Chimney** Rock is a geological rock formation
- **Coufal** site is an archaeological site
- USS **Hazard** (AM-240) was a minesweeper
- **Leary** Site is an archaeological site near Rulo
- **Palmer** Site is also called Skidi Pawnee Village
- **Robidoux** Pass is a gap through Wildcat Hills
- Fort **Robinson** is a former U.S. Army fort
- **Schultz** Site is also known as Mira Creek Site
- **Walker** Gilmore Site was declared in 1964

NEVADA CITIES 55

```
Z  C  R  C  S  P  A  R  K  S
H  M  R  V  W  E  L  L  S  Y
E  D  N  E  Q  B  L  M  F  C
N  F  E  R  N  L  E  Y  C  A
D  P  L  R  Y  O  L  X  W  R
E  S  K  F  A  L  L  O  N  L
R  I  O  Z  C  S  M  Z  O  I
S  M  E  S  Q  U  I  T  E  N
O  F  N  H  T  K  Q  Y  P  P
N  T  Q  X  G  B  T  P  S  A
```

- **Henderson** is the location of Lake Las Vegas
- **Elko** is where the real cowboys of Nevada are
- **Fallon** was once called the Oasis of Nevada
- **Fernley** was the early Amazon.com center
- **Mesquite** is located in the Virgin River valley
- **Ely** was founded as a stagecoach station
- **Reno** is known for its tourism industry
- **Sparks** was named after a Nevada Governor
- **Carlin** was named after a Civil War general
- **Wells** lays in the heart of the Ruby Mountains

NEVADA LANDMARKS

```
V  C  F  R  A  N  C  I  S  G
C  H  U  R  C  H  I  L  L  R
I  E  T  R  K  I  M  I  K  A
U  C  H  A  R  C  O  A  L  I
H  L  E  O  N  A  R  D  F  L
O  P  K  R  Z  E  M  U  U  W
O  L  Y  D  O  I  O  B  B  A
V  O  P  O  B  U  N  A  R  Y
E  W  L  O  V  E  L  O  C  K
R  S  T  O  K  E  S  S  V  K
```

- Ward **Charcoal** Ovens State Historic Park
- Fort **Churchill** was built in 1860
- **Francis** G. Newlands Home is a historic house
- **Hoover** Dam is a concrete arch-gravity dam
- **Leonard** Rockshelter is a prehistoric site
- **Lovelock** Cave is an archaeological site
- Old Las Vegas **Mormon** Fort State Historic Park
- Nevada Northern **Railway** Museum
- Fort **Ruby** was built in 1862
- **Stokes** Castle is a three-story stone tower

NEW HAMPSHIRE CITIES

```
G  P  D  O  V  E  R  L  C  M
R  O  C  H  E  S  T  E  R  A
U  R  W  Q  N  U  G  B  K  N
S  T  K  E  E  N  E  A  N  C
T  S  B  E  R  L  I  N  A  H
R  M  E  U  R  Z  R  O  S  E
C  O  N  C  O  R  D  N  H  S
E  U  A  Y  V  K  K  E  U  T
P  T  X  T  Q  E  T  U  A  E
V  H  L  A  C  O  N  I  A  R
```

- **Concord** is the capital city of the state
- **Berlin** is known for Nansen Ski Jump
- **Manchester** has humid continental climate
- **Dover** is home to Woodman Institute Museum
- **Rochester,** largest city in the seacoast region
- **Lebanon** is the smallest city of the state
- **Keene** is known for producing wooden-ware
- **Laconia** was once known for Pumpkin Festival
- **Nashua** is called Best Place to Live in America
- **Portsmouth** is known for tax-free shopping

NEW HAMPSHIRE LANDMARKS

```
J  W  E  N  T  W  O  R  T  H
G  O  I  L  A  D  D  A  H  Y
S  R  S  E  L  X  O  U  K  M
U  O  C  I  B  E  Z  G  X  S
L  B  A  J  A  T  Z  U  C  Q
L  E  R  J  C  H  N  S  C  J
I  R  T  H  O  R  N  T  O  N
V  T  S  C  R  M  O  U  N  T
A  D  F  X  E  X  Z  S  V  N
N  M  W  E  B  S  T  E  R  V
```

- USS **Albacore** is a unique research submarine
- **Augustus** Saint-Gaudens Memorial
- **Josiah** Bartlett House is a house in Kingston
- **Ladd** Gilman House was built in 1755
- **Mount** Washington Hotel is in Bretton Woods
- **Robert** Frost Farm is located in Derry
- John **Sullivan** House is a historic house
- Matthew **Thornton** House is on 2.5 acres
- Daniel **Webster** Family Home was built in 1829
- **Wentworth** Coolidge Mansion is in Portsmouth

NEW JERSEY CITIES

```
P  E  L  I  Z  A  B  E  T  H
A  B  E  C  L  E  C  M  Q  C
T  A  X  X  L  I  O  M  Y  A
E  Y  N  O  A  I  N  C  D  M
R  O  E  U  N  K  F  D  D  D
S  N  W  D  B  E  W  T  E  E
O  N  A  T  R  E  N  T  O  N
N  E  R  H  O  B  O  K  E  N
C  C  K  V  D  Y  L  Y  J  R
P  L  A  I  N  F  I  E  L  D
```

- **Trenton** is the capital city of the state
- **Bayonne** is known for refining crude oil
- **Camden** was incorporated in 1828
- **Clifton** is located along the Passaic River
- **Elizabeth** is New Jersey's first capital city
- **Hoboken** saw the first baseball recorded game
- **Newark** is the cultural center of the state
- **Paterson** is known as the Silk City
- **Plainfield** is nicknamed as the Queen City
- **Linden** is regional hub of Polish immigration

NEW JERSEY LANDMARKS

```
S  E  A  B  R  I  G  H  T  P
G  M  X  O  J  Q  C  U  C  R
B  A  N  A  S  S  A  U  K  I
O  Y  P  M  A  T  M  D  B  N
X  B  D  N  N  Z  P  O  O  C
W  U  R  A  D  B  U  R  N  E
O  R  E  V  Y  A  H  V  C  T
O  Y  X  A  O  Q  J  E  W  O
D  O  C  E  M  O  R  V  E  N
G  R  I  N  G  W  O  O  D  I
```

- **Boxwood** Hall is a historic house museum
- **Camp** Evans Historic District is near Belmar
- **Maybury** Hill is Joseph Hewes's boyhood home
- **Morven** served as the governor's mansion
- **Nassau** Hall served as US Capitol building
- **Princeton** Battlefield covers 681 acres
- **Radburn** is an unincorporated community
- **Ringwood** Manor was the site of ironworks
- **Sandy** Hook Lighthouse was built in 1764
- **Seabright** Lawn Tennis and Cricket Club

NEW MEXICO CITIES

```
L O R D S B U R G G
M P E U N I C E R A
F O W J J C I F O M
D R C L O V I S S O
T T J Q A G W I W R
R A T O N R U H E I
K L E S P A N O L A
I E V J W N K B L R
C S H M D T H B T T
S O Y O F S K S T Y
```

- **Espanola** was called the first capital city in US
- **Clovis** is located in southeastern Curry County
- **Grants** is gateway to several national parks
- **Hobbs** was founded by James Isaac Hobbs
- **Lordsburg** is a city in northern Hidalgo County
- **Moriarty** is called Crossroads of Opportunity
- **Portales** is known for dairy products
- **Eunice** was founded in 1909 for ranchers
- **Raton** is located in south of Raton Pass
- **Roswell** is known for aerospace engineering

NEW MEXICO LANDMARKS

```
R W X U J Y C P T M
B A N D E L I E R A
C G C S W K F C Y N
A O R O R K O O A U
R N Q L M U L S B E
L O Q B Y A S P L L
S A N D I A O C M I
B P U R B L M Q A T
A M E S I L L A H O
D E G L O R I E T A
```

- **Acoma** Pueblo is a Native American pueblo
- **Bandelier** National Monument, created in 1916
- **Carlsbad** Irrigation District covers 5,464 acres
- **Folsom** Site is a major archaeological site
- **Glorieta** Pass Battlefield was site of Civil War
- **Manuelito** Complex was declared in 1964
- **Mesilla** Plaza is central plaza in Mesilla town
- **Pecos** National Historical Park in Pecos village
- **Sandia** Cave is also called Sandia Man Cave
- **Wagon** Mound is a butte on Santa Fe Trail

NEW YORK CITIES

```
A A H B A T A V I A
Q S Y R A C U S E M
A N O R W I C H K S
B L I T F S O D I T
U P B T P H H O N E
F T W A F H O G G R
F Y Y O N K E R S D
A T Q M Q Y S W T A
L K H O E T A J O M
O L C H U D S O N C
```

- **Albany** is the capital city of the state
- **Amsterdam** lies along the Mohawk River
- **Batavia** is celebrated for its rich heritage
- **Buffalo** has the world's largest flour milling
- **Cohoes** is called the Spindle City
- **Hudson** lies on the east side of Hudson River
- **Kingston** became New York's first capital city
- **Norwich** took its name from Norwich, England
- **Syracuse** is economic hub of Central New York
- **Yonkers** is known as the City of Seven Hills

NEW YORK LANDMARKS

```
C C J S K N G P X T
H L U H V I N R L B
R E B C X A S B E G
I R V G R G N S W E
S M A N H A T T A N
T O X J F R I E R E
E N K X X A F L O S
E T S K R O S C O E
N B O U G H T O N O
C M H H A R M O N Y
```

- **Boughton** Hill is Native American historic site
- **Christeen** is the oldest oyster sloop in US
- **Clermont** is located in Tivoli village
- Fort **Crailo** is also called Yankee Doodle House
- **Geneseo** Historic District was founded in 1790
- **Harmony** Mills was worlds largest cotton mill
- Villa **Lewaro** is a 20,000-square-foot mansion
- Lower **Manhattan** has many historic buildings
- **Niagara** Falls State Park was created in 1885
- **Roscoe** Conkling House is a historic house

NORTH CAROLINA CITIES

```
E   Y   P   R   S   V   G   M   S   S
H   C   T   A   L   J   A   E   H   A
I   O   V   L   I   D   S   W   E   L
C   N   Y   E   U   O   T   X   L   I
K   C   W   I   L   S   O   N   B   S
O   O   J   G   T   T   N   F   Y   B
R   R   I   H   R   C   I   Z   B   U
Y   D   D   U   R   H   A   M   N   R
C   H   A   R   L   O   T   T   E   Y
W   K   I   N   S   T   O   N   D   K
```

- **Raleigh** is the capital city of the state
- **Charlotte** is most populous city of the state
- **Concord** won All-America City Award in 2004
- **Durham** is leader in health-related activities
- **Gastonia** is known for textile manufacturing
- **Hickory** is located in western Catawba County
- **Kinston** is situated along the Neuse River
- **Salisbury** is noted for its historic preservation
- **Shelby** is known as home to Shelby Dynasty
- **Wilson** is the birthplace of Truist Financial

NORTH CAROLINA LANDMARKS

```
H  A  Y  E  S  C  C  X  B  C
Q  S  U  P  L  K  H  T  Z  O
F  G  U  I  L  F  O  R  D  O
C  Q  Z  N  O  J  W  Y  Y  L
S  A  L  E  M  X  A  O  D  M
A  W  P  H  L  E  N  N  G  O
Z  O  C  U  P  O  L  A  L  R
K  H  A  R  D  A  W  A  Y  E
D  V  H  S  L  A  F  C  C  K
G  D  V  T  T  A  V  E  R  N
```

- **Chowan** County Courthouse was built in 1767
- **Coolmore** is a historic plantation house
- **Cupola** House is a historic house museum
- **Guilford** Courthouse National Military Park
- **Hardaway** Site is an archaeological site
- **Hayes** Plantation is also known as Hayes Farm
- **Pinehurst** is a village in Moore County
- **Salem** Tavern is a historic museum
- Union **Tavern** is a historic tavern in Milton
- **Tryon** Palace is located in New Bern city

NORTH DAKOTA CITIES

```
W  I  L  L  I  S  T  O  N  U
F  M  U  M  A  N  D  A  N  W
H  A  R  V  E  Y  F  B  H  A
T  W  R  B  E  I  B  I  C  H
J  G  M  G  H  L  K  S  B  P
U  B  H  H  O  A  V  M  E  E
D  W  A  G  R  I  R  A  U  T
U  O  Z  I  A  F  K  R  L  O
V  Q  E  A  C  F  Z  C  A  N
I  Q  N  K  E  M  R  K  H  H
```

- **Bismarck** is the capital city of the state
- **Beulah** has the largest lignite mine in US
- **Fargo** sits on western bank of Red River
- **Harvey** was founded in 1893 as division point
- **Hazen** offers activities like archery, biking etc.
- **Horace** has one of the oldest post office
- **Mandan** is on Morton County's eastern border
- **Velva** has a humid continental climate
- **Wahpeton** lies on the Bois de Sioux River
- **Williston** is home to Williston State College

NORTH DAKOTA LANDMARKS

```
K U L Y N C H V M T
I A U Q P O O T E Y
L H I D A T S A N T
L F C U E S A U O H
D Y U H U F F L K E
E M N I A G Q Z E O
E U I T O T V E N D
R N O J U Y E V W O
O H N M A N D A N R
L A W R E N C E U E
```

- **Chateau** de Mores is situated near Medora city
- Big **Hidatsa** Village Site lies near Stanton city
- **Huff** Archeological Site is near Huff town
- **Killdeer** Mountain Battlefield Historic Site
- **Lawrence** Welk Birthplace is in Strasburg city
- **Lynch** Quarry Site was a major source of flint
- Fort **Mandan** was encampment near Washburn
- **Menoken** Site is an archeological site
- **Theodore** Roosevelt National Park
- Fort **Union** Trading Post National Historic Site

OHIO CITIES

```
L O R A I N W R Y I
A L L I A N C E E P
I J D K P B O D T A
M S C N W B L Q L R
A S H T A B U L A M
U M E O Y Q M V K A
M N V L M K B O R Z
E U I E M R U N O E
E Y O D E W S A N O
X J T O B R Y A N G
```

- **Columbus** is the capital city of the state
- **Akron** is called Rubber Capital of the World
- **Alliance** is known as the Carnation City
- **Ashtabula** is at the mouth of Ashtabula River
- **Bryan** is known as the Fountain City
- **Cheviot** is called the Heart of The West Side
- **Lorain** has over 70 different nationalities
- **Maumee** got declared All-America City in 2006
- **Parma** ranked as US third safest city in 2014
- **Toledo** is called the Glass Capital of The World

OHIO LANDMARKS 70

```
U V C B J Y O J O H
M E L D E A N O B O
A S E R P E N T E P
N W V V M W W I R E
A D E N A S B J L W
S J L A A P P S I E
S H A W T H O R N L
E K N Z T K E F Y L
H V D S H E R M A N
R U T H E R F O R D
```

- **Adena** Mansion was completed in 1807
- **Cleveland** Arcade was built in 1890
- **Eldean** Covered Bridge is a historic bridge
- **Hawthorn** Hill is situated in Oakwood city
- **Hopewell** Culture National Historical Park
- **Manasseh** Cutler Hall was built in 1819
- **Oberlin** College is a private liberal arts college
- **Rutherford** B. Hayes House is in Fremont
- Great **Serpent** Mound is 1,348 foot long
- John **Sherman** Birthplace is a house museum

OKLAHOMA CITIES

```
M  R  M  S  H  A  W  N  E  E
A  R  D  M  O  R  E  T  Q  U
K  S  M  U  S  K  O  G  E  E
S  T  I  L  L  W  A  T  E  R
E  F  T  L  J  O  P  U  D  G
Y  B  O  A  T  Y  O  L  M  X
E  U  O  W  C  Y  C  S  O  U
N  I  K  T  A  Y  I  A  N  K
I  R  M  O  O  R  E  X  D  V
D  V  H  N  N  T  G  B  K  X
```

- **Tulsa** was called the Oil Capital of the World
- **Ardmore** is world's largest inland cotton port
- **Edmond** is known for great education
- **Enid** holds the nickname of Queen Wheat City
- **Lawton** is known for huge granite deposits
- **Moore** is popular for frequent tornadoes
- **Muskogee** lies in the Arkansas River Valley
- **Shawnee** is called Redbud City of Oklahoma
- **Stillwater** lies in the area called Tornado Alley
- **Yukon** was founded by A.N. Spencer in 1891

OKLAHOMA LANDMARKS

```
L F H E A V E N E R
K G N B I Z Z E L L
L I I I S P B Y B O
W B J M C Q Y E O C
A S O A U H P W L R
S O C H E R O K E E
H N K Q H B R L Y E
I G U T H R I E S K
T Y J A K A D Y L A
A J F K U O L V I L
```

- **Bizzell** Memorial Library is in Norman city
- **Boley** Historic District was founded in 1903
- **Cherokee** National Capitol is a historic building
- Camp **Nichols** is also known as Fort Nichols
- Deer **Creek** site lies near Newkirk city
- Fort **Gibson** is a historic military site
- **Guthrie** Historic District covers 31-acre area
- **Heavener** Runestone is in Le Flore County
- George M. **Murrell** Home is a house museum
- **Washita** Battlefield National Historic Site

OREGON CITIES (73)

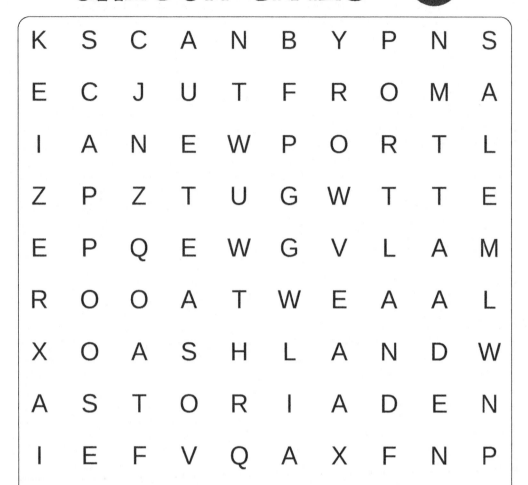

K S C A N B Y P N S
E C J U T F R O M A
I A N E W P O R T L
Z P Z T U G W T T E
E P Q E W G V L A M
R O O A T W E A A L
X O A S H L A N D W
A S T O R I A D E N
I E F V Q A X F N P
P E N D L E T O N L

- **Salem** is the capital city of the state
- **Ashland** is home to OSF festival
- **Astoria** is the oldest city in Oregon
- **Canby** experiences warm and dry summers
- **Eugene** is home to the University of Oregon
- **Keizer** is named after a settler, Thomas Keizur
- **Newport** is home to Oregon Coast Aquarium
- **Pendleton** is famous for its woolen mills
- **Portland** is known as a shipping port
- **Scappoose** was home to a shoe factory

OREGON LANDMARKS

```
W  O  P  T  U  P  V  L  K  T
A  S  T  O  R  I  A  I  G  I
L  M  I  J  C  T  Q  G  S  M
L  A  L  M  V  T  E  H  U  B
O  R  L  Y  A  O  P  T  N  E
W  I  A  G  S  C  K  S  K  R
A  T  M  A  O  K  M  H  E  L
P  I  O  N  E  E  R  I  N  I
M  M  O  B  X  E  T  P  M  N
U  E  K  L  A  M  A  T  H  E
```

- Fort **Astoria**, at the entrance to Columbus River
- Lower **Klamath** National Wildlife Refuge
- United States **lightship** Columbia is in Astoria
- Columbia River **Maritime** Museum
- **Pioneer** Courthouse is a federal courthouse
- **Pittock** Mansion was originally built in 1914
- **Sunken** Village Archeological Site
- **Tillamook** Rock Light, a deactivated lighthouse
- **Timberline** Lodge is a mountain lodge
- **Wallowa** Lake is a Native American cemetery

PENNSYLVANIA CITIES

```
N   H   J   W   A   R   R   E   N   A
F   A   R   E   A   D   I   N   G   D
P   R   G   W   S   C   C   K   W   Y
I   R   V   G   H   H   O   X   T   T
T   I   J   L   A   E   E   R   A   V
T   S   O   T   R   S   T   R   R   M
S   B   Q   C   O   T   W   M   M   Y
T   U   C   K   N   E   R   I   E   N
O   R   O   Y   O   R   K   Z   O   S
N   G   S   C   R   A   N   T   O   N
```

- **Harrisburg** is the capital city of the state
- **Chester** is the oldest city in Pennsylvania
- **Erie** is known as the Flagship City
- **Corry** became famous for Climax locomotives
- **Pittston** is situated in Greater Pittston region
- **Reading** has been known as The Pretzel City
- **Scranton** is nicknamed as Electric City
- **Sharon** area was first settled in 1795
- **Warren** is named after General Joseph Warren
- **York** is also known as the White Rose City

PENNSYLVANIA LANDMARKS

```
C  W  B  P  U  L  P  I  T  R
E  B  C  O  A  Y  H  L  W  L
D  H  A  U  S  Z  H  Z  H  D
A  G  R  E  Y  T  A  S  A  A
R  I  R  H  A  S  Q  T  R  C
C  F  I  E  P  H  R  A  T  A
R  F  E  M  W  M  E  P  O  X
O  O  M  L  O  P  B  L  N  S
F  R  O  I  G  Q  P  E  P  T
T  D  I  V  U  B  E  T  H  D
```

- **Beth** Sholom Congregation was built in 1959
- **Bost** Building is also known as Columbia Hotel
- **Carrie** Furnace is a former blast furnace
- **Cedarcroft** is also called Bayard Taylor House
- **Ephrata** Cloister was a religious community
- **Gifford** Pinchot House was built in 1886
- **Grey** Towers Castle was designated in 1985
- **Pulpit** Rocks is a geological formation
- **Staple** Bend Tunnel was US first railway tunnel
- **Wharton** Esherick Studio was built in 1926

RHODE ISLAND CITIES

```
K A W A R W I C K E E
F C C Q T Q M D J X
P R O V I D E N C E
G A V U V I B F N T
W N E K E F R I E E
H S N K R O I Q W R
F T T K T S S V P O
E O R Q O T T N O Z
L N Y L N F O P R J
W E S T E R L Y T C
```

- **Providence** is the capital city of the state
- **Bristol** is named after Bristol, England
- **Coventry** was first settled by English colonists
- **Cranston** was once known as Pawtuxet
- **Exeter** was founded in 1742
- **Foster** has state's authentic covered bridge
- **Newport** is famous for its mansions
- **Tiverton** was home of Fall River Marksmen
- **Warwick** has state's main airport T. F. Green
- **Westerly** is a popular tourist destination

RHODE ISLAND LANDMARKS

```
F  A  K  O  G  F  J  B  M  J
X  L  I  Q  I  F  R  A  A  S
F  D  N  S  L  A  T  E  R  R
G  R  G  M  B  L  U  N  B  E
V  I  S  T  E  C  Q  X  L  D
E  C  C  U  R  H  N  T  E  W
R  H  O  J  T  O  W  B  D  O
N  D  T  H  U  N  T  E  R  O
O  B  E  I  L  E  V  U  E  D
N  H  C  R  E  S  C  E  N  T
```

- Nelson W. **Aldrich** House is in Providence
- **Bellevue** Avenue Historic District is in Newport
- **Crescent** Park Looff Carousel was built in 1895
- **Gilbert** Stuart Birthplace and Museum
- **Hunter** House is a historic house in Newport
- **Kingscote** is a Gothic Revival mansion
- **Marble** House is a Gilded Age mansion
- **Redwood** Library and Athenaeum
- **Slater** Mill is a historic textile mill complex
- **Vernon** House is a historic house in Newport

SOUTH CAROLINA CITIES

```
V  E  C  F  J  G  Y  G  A  G
C  A  Y  C  E  X  R  R  I  K
S  S  A  L  Q  C  L  E  K  R
U  L  N  I  Y  O  V  E  E  A
M  E  D  N  D  L  I  N  N  R
T  Y  E  T  L  U  H  V  Z  M
E  U  R  O  O  M  N  I  F  E
R  A  S  N  L  B  Y  L  L  Y
M  F  O  J  I  I  J  L  B  I
H  A  N  A  H  A  N  E  I  G
```

- **Columbia** is the capital city of the state
- **Anderson** is known as the City of Hospitality
- **Clinton** is the home of Presbyterian College
- **Aiken** is named after a railroad president
- **Cayce** has several hiking trails throughout
- **Easley** is known for Big League World Series
- **Greenville** is popular as a cultural center
- **Greer** is home to South Carolina Inland Port
- **Hanahan** is known for fishing and water sports
- **Sumter's** is known for its biotech industry

SOUTH CAROLINA LANDMARKS

```
F  M  I  L  L  F  O  R  D  V
L  E  H  Z  Z  Q  O  R  H  E
X  P  I  D  B  H  K  I  O  M
N  E  B  O  R  O  U  G  H  A
X  A  E  T  O  T  Y  U  F  N
W  C  R  E  B  S  W  C  P  U
V  H  N  U  I  N  D  X  E  E
P  O  I  N  S  E  T  T  N  L
D  I  A  Z  A  E  X  O  N  W
C  D  N  P  O  M  P  I  O  N
```

- **Borough** House Plantation is in Stateburg
- James Petigru **Boyce** Chapel, a historic church
- **Emanuel** African Methodist Episcopal Church
- **Hibernian** Hall is a historic meeting hall
- **Millford** Plantation covers 712-acre area
- **Peachoid** is a 135-feet-tall water tower
- **Penn** Center was formerly the Penn School
- Westin **Poinsett** Hotel is a twelve-story hotel
- **Pompion** Hill Chapel is a back parish church
- **Snee** Farm plantation is in Mount Pleasant

SOUTH DAKOTA CITIES

```
B  R  A  N  D  O  N  R  K  Q
W  R  T  V  W  A  R  N  E  R
V  O  L  G  A  H  W  H  N  M
B  H  H  G  T  I  U  D  J  I
I  L  P  I  E  R  R  E  J  L
S  P  E  A  R  F  I  S  H  B
F  P  S  K  T  J  K  E  V  A
T  H  U  R  O  N  R  Q  B  N
E  H  X  H  W  G  O  N  O  K
A  F  L  A  N  D  R  E  A  U
```

- **Pierre** is the capital city of the state
- **Brandon** had its name from Brandon Township
- **Flandreau** is located along the Big Sioux River
- **Huron** is home to the South Dakota State Fair
- **Milbank** is named after a railroad director
- **Spearfish** lies at the base of the Black Hills
- **Tea** was named after tradition of drinking tea
- **Volga** is mentioned in a juvenile novel
- **Warner** is named after a settler, Warren Tarbox
- **Watertown** is home to the Redlin Art Center

SOUTH DAKOTA LANDMARKS

```
D E A D W O O D V N
R Y M W O U N D E D
U P I E R R E Z R I
S J N F R A W L E Y
H D U D R U B K N F
M I T C H E L L D I
O Z E A K Z O Q R I
R Q M T L Q O U Y C
E D A E M F M X E C
O R N M O L S T A D
```

- **Bloom** Site is an archaeological site
- **Deadwood** Historic District had dead trees
- **Frawley** Ranch is a historic ranch
- **Minuteman** Missile National Historic Site
- **Mitchell** Site is an archaeological site
- **Molstad** Village was declared in 1964
- Fort **Pierre** Chouteau was a major trading post
- Mount **Rushmore** National Memorial
- **Verendrye** Site was declared in 1991
- **Wounded** Knee Battlefield, (Dec 29, 1890)

TENNESSEE CITIES

```
B A R T L E T T P W
J K F G A Z L K P E
Z I R V P Y X L B M
Z N A S H V I L L E
R G N L L P I A M M
C S K G O Q F L A P
R P L F J U Z G R H
U O I I B O D O T I
M R N G T M X O I S
P T C O W A N D N I
```

- **Nashville** is the capital city of the state
- **Algood** is known for its poultry business
- **Bartlett** was originally called the Union Depot
- **Cowan** was founded in late 18th century
- **Crump** is located in western Hardin County
- **Franklin** is home of several historic buildings
- **Kingsport** is known for plastics production
- **Loudon** has a humid subtropical climate
- **Martin** is named for Captain William Martin
- **Memphis** is located along the Mississippi River

TENNESSEE LANDMARKS

```
F  R  A  N  K  L  I  N  D  W
M  X  C  B  R  Y  M  A  N  Y
A  E  D  R  L  M  D  B  Q  N
S  Y  C  A  M  O  R  E  O  N
O  O  Y  T  X  C  U  R  P  E
N  T  G  T  L  C  I  N  C  W
I  U  Z  L  T  A  Z  R  T  O
C  J  S  E  M  S  Z  G  X  O
X  U  J  U  B  I  L  E  E  D
P  I  N  S  O  N  T  H  S  L
```

- **Blount** Mansion is located in Knoxville
- **Franklin** Battlefield was declared in 1960
- **Jubilee** Hall was completed in 1876
- Hiram **Masonic** Lodge No. 7 is in Franklin
- **Moccasin** Bend Archeological District
- **Pinson** Mounds complex is in Madison County
- **Rattle** and Snap is a plantation estate
- **Ryman** Auditorium has 2,362 seats
- **Sycamore** Shoals of the Watauga River
- **Wynnewood** is also called Castalian Springs

TEXAS CITIES (85)

```
F  R  E  E  R  Q  O  S  H  H
L  P  C  P  O  B  P  Y  O  A
Y  H  E  L  O  T  E  S  U  R
D  U  L  J  A  D  G  J  S  L
E  D  I  N  B  U  R  G  T  I
F  N  N  G  P  B  S  R  O  N
E  A  A  I  P  L  L  T  N  G
W  I  T  I  J  I  X  K  I  E
J  E  T  E  S  N  R  K  M  N
S  F  L  U  B  B  O  C  K  S
```

- **Austin** is the capital city of the state
- **Celina** is among the fastest growing cities
- **Dublin** is the birhtplace of golfer Ben Hogan
- **Edinburg** lies in south-central Hidalgo County
- **Fate** was settled shortly after the Civil War
- **Freer** had the first oil well drilled in the state
- **Harlingen** is located in Rio Grande Valley
- **Helotes** is a small city in Bexar County
- **Houston** is the most populous city of the state
- **Lubbock** is nicknamed as the Hub City

TEXAS LANDMARKS

```
H V E C B U W L X O
A H J O H D Z R P Q
R L A N D E R G I N
R U C C A A D B D E
E D I H J L X R D S
L C N O M E A O X P
L P T C L Y T M T A
F P O K D H R A O D
F R A N D O L P H A
S P I N D L E T O P
```

- **Alamo** Mission in San Antonio
- Fort **Concho** is a former US Army installation
- **Dealey** Plaza is a city park in downtown Dallas
- **Espada** Acequia was built by Franciscan friars
- **Harrell** Site is also called the M.D. Harrell Site
- San **Jacinto** Battleground State Historic Site
- **Landergin** Mesa is an archeological site
- **Randolph** Field Historic District
- **Roma** Historic District was established in 1821
- **Spindletop** is an oil field in Beaumont

UTAH CITIES 87

```
N K A Y S V I L L E
D E M L M D L A F B
H N I J O R O Y F O
T I L R R O A T E U
P B L P O Z E O V N
P L C K N N P N P T
H E R R I M A N R I
X Y E S J L P T O F
R A E J W A M Q V U
X I K D E L T A O L
```

- **Kaysville** is situated in the Davis County
- **Bountiful** was incorporated in 1892
- **Delta** was originally a railroad switch
- **Herriman** was established by Henry Harriman
- **Layton** is a leader in economic development
- **Millcreek** is a small city in Salt Lake County
- **Moroni** is home to Moroni Feed Company
- **Nibley** is known for celebrating Heritage Days
- **Provo** is known for technology development
- **Roy** is known for Bank of Utah's first branch

UTAH LANDMARKS

U	K	G	S	H	Q	R	W	G	H
X	R	U	B	I	N	G	H	A	M
D	E	S	O	L	A	T	I	O	N
O	E	B	Q	U	A	R	R	Y	Z
U	D	R	W	C	L	D	Q	D	R
G	O	I	C	D	K	A	S	E	M
L	P	G	O	C	A	N	Y	O	N
A	S	H	A	A	L	G	E	I	K
S	T	A	P	F	I	E	E	G	D
J	X	M	X	V	B	R	Y	C	E

- **Alkali** Ridge is also known as Alkali Point
- **Bingham** Canyon Mine has open-pit mining
- **Brigham** Young Complex has historic buildings
- **Bryce** Canyon Lodge is a lodging facility
- Emigration **Canyon** is in Salt Lake County
- **Danger** Cave is an archaeological site
- **Desolation** Canyon lies on the Green River
- Camp **Douglas** was established in 1862
- **Reed** O. Smoot House is located in Provo city
- **Quarry** Visitor Center was declared in 2001

VERMONT CITIES

```
H  H  X  X  M  F  B  P  B  W
M  I  L  T  O  N  S  O  A  I
S  S  T  T  N  I  W  W  R  N
H  L  L  C  T  T  A  N  T  O
E  L  D  A  P  H  N  A  O  O
L  G  P  S  E  I  T  L  N  S
D  G  U  I  L  F  O  R  D  K
O  W  V  N  I  S  N  N  T  I
N  F  S  X  F  B  A  R  R  E
L  J  H  A  R  T  L  A  N  D
```

- **Montpelier** is the capital city of the state
- **Barre** is called the Granite Center of the World
- **Barton** had its first train arrival in 1863
- **Guilford** is located in Windham County
- **Hartland** was known for blanket mills
- **Milton** was chartered by Benning Wentworth
- **Pownal** was known for horse racing
- **Sheldon** is located in central Franklin County
- **Swanton** was gifted Royal Swans in 1961
- **Winooski** is known as the Mill City

VERMONT LANDMARKS

```
S O C I A L I S T X
T N M O U N T N B C
E J A A W Q D Y M Q
L U D U P I H P P M
L S H E L B U R N E
A T A M C A L V I N
F I M M H E K U H B
A N W A W S U H P D
N V R O B E R T A N
E G M C R O K E B Y
```

- President **Calvin** Coolidge State Historical Site
- **Emma** Willard House is a historic house
- **Justin** Smith Morrill Homestead is in Strafford
- **Mount** Independence lies on Lake Champlain
- **Naulakha** is also called Rudyard Kipling House
- **Robert** Frost Farm is on 150-acre area
- **Rokeby** Museum is a historic farm property
- **Shelburne** Farms, a non-profit education center
- **Socialist** Labor Party Hall was built in 1900
- **Stellafane** is a clubhouse in Springfield

VIRGINIA CITIES 91

F Y S G A L A X U R
A L T O G N O G R I
I S A L E M E M A C
R S U F F O L K D H
F H N S N D T Z F M
A J T N L O C T O O
X S O H U T R P R N
E V N D Y K K T D D
T N U H A M P T O N
L E E S B U R G Z N

- **Richmond** is the capital city of the state
- **Fairfax** derives its name from Thomas Fairfax
- **Galax** is known for furniture manufacturing
- **Leesburg** was the site of Battle of Ball's Bluff
- **Radford** is known for its beautiful scenery
- **Norton** is known for historic Hotel Norton
- **Salem** is home of Roanoke College
- **Hampton** is known for industrial enterprises
- **Suffolk** was founded by English colonists
- **Staunton** is the birthplace of Woodrow Wilson

VIRGINIA LANDMARKS

```
M O N T I C E L L O
C W I K Y W S H M M
P W T O O Y H O R A
E D G A R T I Y I N
Q Y Y I K H R Q P A
D Q K Z T E L E S S
K E N M O R E R H S
Y R A D W E Y H I A
A R L I N G T O N S
Z S T O N E W A L L
```

- **Arlington** Historical Museum, founded in 1962
- **Edgar** Allan Poe Museum is in Richmond
- **Kenmore** is also known as Kenmore Plantation
- **Manassas** National Battlefield Park
- **Monticello** was built in 1772
- **Ripshin** Farm is a historic farm property
- **Shirley** Plantation is located on James River
- **Stonewall** Jackson's Headquarters Museum
- **Wythe** House is historic house in Williamsburg
- Battlefield of **Yorktown,** October 19, 1781

WASHINGTON CITIES

```
V A N C O U V E R R
U K O L Y M P I A R
E W E N A T C H E E
S D V N T S R Q W N
E A E Q T D L K D T
A B R U B V G W U O
T B E L L E V U E N
T A T A C O M A G S
L U T F Z Z Q K G O
E S P O K A N E P Z
```

- **Olympia** is the capital city of the state
- **Bellevue** is called High-Tech and Retail Center
- **Everett** lies at the mouth of Snohomish River
- **Kent** was called Lettuce Capital of the World
- **Renton** is known for Boeing 737 assembling
- **Seattle** is mostly nicknamed as Emerald City
- **Spokane** is the birthplace of Father's Day
- **Tacoma** is known for its glass art
- **Vancouver** is located along the Columbia River
- **Wenatchee** is known for producing apples

WASHINGTON LANDMARKS

```
Z  N  T  O  W  N  S  E  N  D
K  I  Z  W  O  R  D  E  N  P
K  S  E  H  C  X  I  F  U  A
P  Q  F  W  H  I  T  M  A  N
I  U  I  M  I  W  P  M  L  A
O  A  B  E  N  E  W  A  H  M
N  L  O  U  O  N  X  R  N  A
E  L  A  U  O  M  H  M  P  Z
E  Y  R  E  K  F  O  E  R  U
R  E  A  C  T  O  R  S  J  Z
```

- **Benewah** Milk Bottle lies in Spokane County
- **Chinook** Point is a headland in Pacific County
- **Marmes** Rockshelter is an archaeological site
- **Nisqually** River is approximately 81 miles long
- **Panama** Hotel in Seattle was built in 1910
- **Pioneer** Building was completed in 1892
- B **Reactor** was first large-scale nuclear reactor
- Port **Townsend** Historic District
- Walt **Whitman** House is a historic building
- Fort **Worden** Historical State Park

WEST VIRGINIA CITIES

```
M O R G A N T O W N
L O G A N C E J H B
A W U S W F L X E W
P E W B E C K L E Y
H I N T O N I U L I
E R V I E N N A I E
T T E K X R S A N M
L O S D X D J J G Y
O N P H I L I P P I
C H A R L E S T O N
```

- **Charleston** is the capital city of the state
- **Beckley** is known for its tourist attractions
- **Elkins** was previously known as Leadsville
- **Hinton** is situated along the New River
- **Logan** was called the Islands of the Guyandot
- **Morgantown** lies along the Monongahela River
- **Philippi** is the site of the Battle of Philippi
- **Vienna** is home to Jackson Junior High School
- **Weirton** is home to Weirton Steel Corporation
- **Wheeling** became known as the Nail City

WEST VIRGINIA LANDMARKS

```
S  C  L  O  V  E  R  B  G  A
E  A  Q  L  W  V  Y  Z  R  W
Y  M  L  B  E  F  C  V  E  C
C  P  Q  H  S  J  S  F  E  L
R  B  M  A  T  E  W  A  N  Y
E  E  G  G  O  L  V  P  B  U
E  L  B  P  N  K  N  U  R  V
K  L  J  E  V  I  E  F  I  A
Q  U  C  A  R  N  I  F  E  X
V  D  A  V  I  S  T  K  R  E
```

- Alexander **Campbell** Mansion is historic house
- **Carnifex** Ferry Battlefield State Park
- **Clover** Site is archeological site near Lesage
- Grave **Creek** Mound is in Ohio River Valley
- **Davis** and Elkins Historic District
- **Elkins** Coal and Coke Company Historic District
- The **Greenbrier** is resort in Greenbrier County
- **Matewan** Historic District was built in 1893
- **Reber** Radio Telescope is a historic telescope
- **Weston** State Hospital is on 26.5 acres

WISCONSIN CITIES

```
Y  K  W  X  G  B  M  X  M  Q
B  E  L  O  I  T  E  L  E  N
L  N  B  B  A  R  R  O  N  F
F  O  L  Y  P  P  R  W  O  M
L  S  A  P  P  V  I  C  M  A
I  H  D  R  L  R  L  G  O  D
J  A  J  L  E  T  L  S  N  I
E  C  H  E  T  E  K  X  I  S
O  S  H  K  O  S  H  Q  E  O
R  A  C  I  N  E  M  L  T  N
```

- **Madison** is the capital city of the state
- **Appleton** serves as heart of Fox River Valley
- **Barron** is known for fishing and hunting
- **Beloit** is home to Minor League Baseball team
- **Chetek** is a beautiful city in Barron County
- **Kenosha** has a humid continental climate
- **Menomonie** is rich in its natural history
- **Merrill** is located in Lincoln County
- **Oshkosh** is known for children clothing brand
- **Racine** is headquarters of several industries

WISCONSIN LANDMARKS

```
T  A  L  I  E  S  I  N  O  A
M  F  E  R  M  R  V  T  C  Z
I  J  T  I  M  I  I  C  O  T
L  K  U  S  E  L  L  I  N  A
W  G  R  A  I  W  L  T  T  L
A  O  N  C  S  X  A  F  O  A
U  J  E  U  N  T  N  B  T  N
K  B  R  I  S  B  O  I  S  U
E  P  V  M  I  G  I  R  X  Z
E  G  P  D  O  U  S  M  A  N
```

- **Astor** Fur Warehouse is historic fur warehouse
- **Aztalan** State Park is a Wisconsin state park
- **Brisbois** is also called Bernard Brisbois House
- **Dousman** Hotel is a historic hotel
- **Milton** House is a historic building in Milton
- **Milwaukee** City Hall was completed in 1895
- **Oconto** Site was designated in 1961
- **Taliesin** is also known as Taliesin Spring Green
- **Turner** Hall is a historic athletic club facility
- **Villa** Louis is located in Prairie du Chien

WYOMING CITIES

```
F  D  L  A  R  A  M  I  E  B
E  W  R  A  F  C  V  U  U  P
G  O  S  K  N  O  N  G  W  O
W  R  Q  H  Y  D  L  G  K  W
O  L  C  H  E  Y  E  N  N  E
C  A  S  P  E  R  H  R  R  L
Z  N  R  A  W  L  I  N  S  L
L  D  G  T  U  N  S  D  T  P
Q  G  N  H  U  G  M  M  A  N
E  V  A  N  S  T  O  N  U  N
```

- **Cheyenne** is the capital city of the state
- **Casper** is nicknamed as The Oil City
- **Cody** is served by Yellowstone Regional Airport
- **Evanston** was named after a civil engineer
- **Laramie** is known for low taxes
- **Lander** is known for its tourist attractions
- **Powell** was a part of the Shoshone Project
- **Rawlins** was known for a major train station
- **Sheridan** is named for General Philip Sheridan
- **Worland** is located along the Big Horn River

WYOMING LANDMARKS

```
N  J  U  M  Z  L  W  L  T  G
F  Q  B  U  D  B  A  R  I  U
M  A  V  R  V  T  P  B  X  E
Z  H  M  I  T  N  I  A  H  R
E  X  P  E  D  I  T  I  O  N
B  T  S  O  S  C  I  P  R  S
W  O  B  S  I  D  I  A  N  E
I  M  M  L  V  T  S  U  E  Y
J  A  C  K  S  O  N  T  R  O
E  O  X  L  A  R  A  M  I  E
```

- **Ames** Monument is a large pyramid
- **Expedition** Island is situated on Green River
- **Guernsey** Dam lies on North Platte River
- **Horner** Site is also known as the Creek Site
- **Jackson** Hole is the name of a valley
- Fort **Laramie** covers 833-acre area
- **Murie** Ranch Historic District was built in 1951
- **Obsidian** Cliff is also known as 48YE433
- **Tom** Sun Ranch lies near Alcova
- **Wapiti** lies along North Fork of Shoshone River

ANSWER KEY

01 ALABAMA CITIES

```
X  L  X  G  Z  Z  L  D  Y  F
M  A  D  I  S  O  N  A  G  V
H  U  N  T  S  V  I  L  L  E
O  K  Z  I  V  L  H  E  G  U
O  D  O  T  H  A  N  V  S  F
V  L  R  Y  K  I  G  I  D  A
E  B  O  M  O  B  I  L  E  U
R  A  U  B  U  R  N  L  O  L
D  E  C  A  T  U  R  E  I  A
M  O  N  T  G  O  M  E  R  Y
```

02 ALABAMA LANDMARKS

```
U  W  M  F  B  Y  U  C  H  I
E  I  R  O  A  P  E  R  R  F
Y  L  L  I  R  X  H  N  E  O
S  S  D  D  T  G  X  W  D  E
L  O  E  R  O  G  A  Y  S  B
O  N  X  Y  N  L  C  N  T  F
S  A  T  U  R  N  T  C  O  F
S  U  E  Q  E  D  M  U  N  D
X  E  R  Q  S  C  D  C  E  Q
T  A  N  N  E  H  I  L  L  L
```

03 ALASKA CITIES

```
S  N  F  W  A  S  I  L  L  A
E  K  A  P  B  E  T  H  E  L
L  E  I  E  E  Q  X  G  I  Q
D  T  R  V  A  L  D  E  Z  Q
O  C  B  R  O  D  I  G  G  S
V  H  A  Y  S  L  M  C  S  C
I  I  N  T  J  U  N  E  A  U
A  K  K  L  A  W  O  C  K  N
O  A  S  T  T  K  S  H  V  D
X  N  H  Y  D  A  B  U  R  G
```

01 ALASKA LANDMARKS

```
F  Q  B  S  I  T  K  A  B  G
Z  V  R  Z  A  X  X  X  I  W
A  W  O  L  D  V  X  Z  R  A
N  G  O  B  I  H  O  Y  N  L
A  S  K  A  G  W  A  Y  I  E
N  P  S  Q  E  L  P  L  R  S
G  C  H  A  L  U  K  A  K  I
U  P  O  R  T  H  O  D  O  X
L  M  D  X  X  V  R  D  H  L
A  N  E  N  E  N  A  H  S  F
```

05 ARIZONA CITIES

```
M  H  C  Y  S  E  D  O  N  A
T  E  T  U  C  S  O  N  Q  F
R  O  S  M  O  S  X  A  E  P
X  V  M  A  T  Y  K  K  D  R
E  W  J  B  T  E  M  P  E  E
F  L  A  G  S  T  A  F  F  S
S  U  D  J  D  T  V  S  L  C
H  F  X  J  A  G  O  U  I  O
F  C  C  J  L  K  Z  N  T  T
E  P  H  O  E  N  I  X  E  T
```

06 ARIZONA LANDMARKS

```
A  H  U  A  C  H  U  C  A  W
U  K  H  B  G  S  F  J  H  F
J  L  O  W  E  L  L  E  X  P
B  V  V  S  I  E  R  R  A  U
W  E  G  I  N  M  B  O  H  E
I  N  A  K  I  V  L  M  X  B
H  T  T  H  U  B  B  E  L  L
T  A  L  I  E  S  I  N  K  O
V  N  I  K  T  W  C  A  S  A
N  A  N  X  Y  L  C  V  Y  N
```

07 ARKANSAS CITIES

08 ARKANSAS LANDMARKS

09 CALIFORNIA CITIES

10 CALIFORNIA LANDMARKS

11 COLORADO CITIES

12 COLORADO LANDMARKS

13 CONNECTICUT CITIES

A	D	A	N	B	U	R	Y	G	G
N	N	O	I	L	T	K	F	R	R
O	O	S	S	H	E	L	T	O	N
R	R	I	O	G	L	N	J	T	O
W	W	T	M	N	V	F	N	O	X
I	A	M	E	R	I	D	E	N	B
C	L	U	Z	Y	E	A	M	K	I
H	K	H	A	R	T	F	O	R	D
W	A	T	E	R	B	U	R	Y	C
T	O	R	R	I	N	G	T	O	N

14 CONNECTICUT LANDMARKS

F	R	E	D	E	R	I	C	F	C
N	U	G	V	Z	X	B	Z	U	O
E	G	R	O	V	E	I	A	Q	M
W	K	I	M	B	E	R	L	Y	P
G	R	S	T	F	O	D	B	A	O
A	M	W	W	A	Y	C	I	L	U
T	J	O	A	O	A	R	I	E	N
E	Q	L	I	L	R	A	V	L	C
F	N	D	N	B	N	F	Q	I	E
Q	G	I	L	L	E	T	T	E	T

15 DELAWARE CITIES

P	S	I	N	Q	D	Z	H	S	W
L	E	W	E	S	E	D	A	C	I
R	A	A	W	Q	L	J	R	Q	L
E	F	K	A	U	A	Z	R	M	M
H	O	H	R	Y	W	T	I	I	I
O	R	M	K	F	A	P	N	L	N
B	D	O	V	E	R	X	G	F	G
O	D	V	S	C	E	J	T	O	T
T	T	A	B	R	T	O	R	O	
H	C	A	S	T	L	E	N	D	N

16 DELAWARE LANDMARKS

H	G	R	P	S	P	U	H	Z	H
O	P	B	V	T	X	T	D	M	A
W	N	E	M	O	U	R	S	C	G
A	S	P	E	N	D	A	L	E	L
R	Z	Z	C	U	N	A	T	Y	E
D	N	L	O	M	B	A	R	D	Y
R	S	E	R	K	A	L	M	A	R
I	V	M	B	E	R	Z	C	T	E
C	H	R	I	S	T	I	N	A	L
W	I	N	T	E	R	T	H	U	R

17 FLORIDA CITIES

S	L	P	O	J	M	I	A	M	I
S	Z	E	F	X	X	X	E	Q	C
S	A	N	I	B	E	L	N	Z	L
H	U	S	Y	H	X	G	P	E	E
I	L	A	K	E	L	A	N	D	R
A	F	C	Z	K	T	D	K	B	M
L	V	O	O	R	L	A	N	D	O
E	C	L	J	C	B	F	M	M	N
A	U	A	C	V	O	A	X	P	T
H	A	P	O	P	K	A	G	S	A

18 FLORIDA LANDMARKS

V	Q	Q	X	P	F	L	S	T	C
I	W	M	I	H	L	L	C	U	A
Z	I	G	H	Q	A	A	S	Y	S
C	N	X	Y	E	G	M	Z	H	T
A	D	M	J	L	L	B	H	A	I
Y	O	D	A	D	E	I	U	X	L
A	V	S	R	N	R	A	I	T	L
J	E	F	F	E	R	S	O	N	O
U	R	A	I	L	R	O	A	D	U
V	E	N	E	T	I	A	N	A	L

19 GEORGIA CITIES

H	C	O	L	U	M	B	U	S	B
I	S	R	O	S	W	E	L	L	R
N	M	A	C	X	V	F	D	N	O
E	I	V	V	D	P	C	G	E	O
S	L	X	J	A	D	F	E	W	K
V	T	L	M	J	N	W	I	N	H
I	O	A	T	L	A	N	T	A	A
L	N	P	T	T	M	C	A	N	V
L	A	T	H	E	N	S	V	H	E
E	D	U	N	W	O	O	D	Y	N

20 GEORGIA LANDMARKS

U	A	M	I	C	A	L	O	L	A
F	M	A	U	H	P	Y	C	E	K
O	A	R	E	I	O	S	T	U	O
L	R	S	B	P	O	Q	A	H	L
K	I	H	A	P	P	V	G	A	O
S	E	A	B	E	Q	W	O	R	M
T	T	L	P	W	J	Z	N	D	K
O	T	L	T	A	M	P	A	M	A
N	A	N	D	A	Y	V	V	A	I
R	I	V	E	R	F	R	O	N	T

21 HAWAII CITIES

P	W	A	I	L	U	K	U	G	A
U	A	M	E	L	G	S	X	G	H
K	I	H	O	N	O	L	U	L	U
A	P	K	G	V	U	M	A	A	I
L	A	X	S	U	N	A	O	H	M
A	H	Y	W	K	R	K	I	A	A
N	U	T	W	T	I	A	N	I	N
I	K	A	N	E	O	H	E	N	U
R	T	H	W	H	I	A	E	A	J
Q	N	K	A	P	O	L	E	I	T

22 HAWAII LANDMARKS

P	W	H	E	E	L	E	R	C	X
H	H	T	F	L	L	J	K	W	Z
I	O	L	A	N	I	U	A	I	G
C	N	L	A	H	A	I	N	A	B
K	O	I	I	R	M	I	E	A	S
A	K	F	K	A	U	N	O	L	U
M	O	X	A	T	L	W	H	O	W
G	H	U	T	N	L	C	E	H	N
K	A	L	A	U	P	A	P	A	F
R	U	M	O	O	K	I	N	I	N

23 IDAHO CITIES

E	F	A	P	R	B	H	P	J	H
C	A	L	D	W	E	L	L	V	A
C	R	A	T	H	D	R	U	M	Y
H	S	R	B	N	X	R	T	J	D
U	N	D	M	O	C	K	M	B	E
B	A	M	E	R	I	D	I	A	N
B	M	L	E	W	I	S	T	O	N
U	P	O	R	A	F	O	E	G	H
C	A	P	L	U	M	M	E	R	E
K	R	O	B	E	R	T	S	G	Y

24 IDAHO LANDMARKS

I	N	M	H	E	L	E	M	H	I
N	F	W	A	L	L	A	C	E	Y
X	C	Z	W	G	W	S	K	P	F
L	W	B	K	Z	U	S	O	C	H
Y	B	P	B	V	C	A	M	A	S
K	O	A	I	N	B	Y	W	T	E
T	I	G	L	A	L	A	W	A	G
K	S	U	L	M	B	O	P	L	J
W	E	I	P	P	E	T	L	D	I
K	C	B	Z	A	D	I	M	O	E

25 ILLINOIS CITIES

A	P	H	K	E	C	A	S	E	Y
U	R	S	J	L	H	W	U	W	C
R	I	W	O	G	P	J	Z	J	H
O	R	P	L	I	V	M	Z	D	I
R	A	B	I	N	G	D	O	N	C
A	L	Q	E	E	R	P	C	H	A
R	T	Y	T	V	L	K	I	B	G
R	O	C	K	F	O	R	D	Y	O
G	N	O	F	C	A	N	T	O	N
C	B	E	L	V	I	D	E	R	E

26 ILLINOIS LANDMARKS

R	M	B	J	W	K	R	D	Y	N
K	O	L	P	O	E	V	K	W	A
I	R	E	U	Y	N	C	T	U	U
N	R	L	B	R	N	A	D	X	V
C	O	H	Y	U	I	H	T	R	O
A	W	L	I	N	C	O	L	N	O
I	W	R	R	O	O	K	E	R	Y
D	F	Q	Q	W	T	I	D	Q	Z
M	O	D	O	C	T	A	Y	E	N
B	G	R	O	S	S	E	P	S	N

27 INDIANA CITIES

L	A	F	A	Y	E	T	T	E	G
I	H	S	G	O	S	H	E	N	R
L	A	W	R	E	N	C	E	J	E
P	M	P	C	H	O	E	D	T	E
O	M	Z	A	A	M	H	P	C	N
R	O	S	H	W	R	T	E	H	F
T	N	S	D	R	P	M	G	L	I
A	D	M	U	N	C	I	E	S	E
G	F	I	S	H	E	R	S	L	L
E	E	B	K	O	K	O	M	O	D

28 INDIANA LANDMARKS

G	R	O	T	T	O	X	O	U	M
R	V	C	O	R	Y	D	O	N	A
O	J	Z	L	A	U	L	H	P	D
U	M	H	A	Q	Z	E	C	A	I
S	I	X	N	D	P	V	L	Y	S
F	L	V	I	F	R	I	E	Z	O
L	L	B	E	N	J	A	M	I	N
A	E	B	R	P	J	T	E	X	B
N	R	Y	Z	A	M	C	N	S	O
D	C	A	N	N	E	L	T	O	N

29 IOWA CITIES

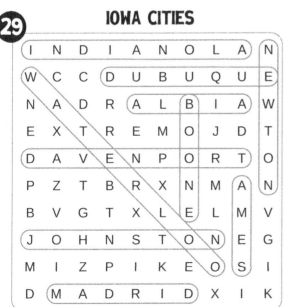

I	N	D	I	A	N	O	L	A	N
W	C	C	D	U	B	U	Q	U	E
N	A	D	R	A	L	B	I	A	W
E	X	T	R	E	M	O	J	D	T
D	A	V	E	N	P	O	R	T	O
P	Z	T	B	R	X	N	M	A	N
B	V	G	T	X	L	E	L	M	V
J	O	H	N	S	T	O	N	E	G
M	I	Z	P	I	K	E	O	S	I
D	M	A	D	R	I	D	X	I	K

30 IOWA LANDMARKS

T	E	R	R	A	C	E	J	D	N
S	E	Q	I	K	E	Q	G	U	H
E	W	C	P	L	F	M	A	B	R
R	O	P	Y	H	F	L	S	U	K
G	O	J	U	L	I	E	N	Q	I
E	D	G	H	K	G	P	U	U	M
A	B	B	I	E	Y	R	P	E	B
N	U	I	J	R	N	Z	R	S	A
T	R	F	S	D	V	Z	P	V	L
C	Y	H	E	R	B	E	R	T	L

KANSAS CITIES

KANSAS LANDMARKS

KENTUCKY CITIES

KENTUCKY LANDMARKS

LOUISIANA CITIES

LOUISIANA LANDMARKS

37 MAINE CITIES

```
I R A C A R I B O U
H W B U U B D D Y B
A E S V G J A J G I
L S S R B U N T G D
L T J B R S S V H D
O B D C E T A T Q E
W R I J W X C C A F
E O H U E Q O T R O
L O G A R D I N E R
L K W S A N F O R D
```

38 MAINE LANDMARKS

```
M C I N T I R E V K
C X K E N T R Q C E
U Y P W P A T H S N
S J E E Q D A A H N
H A R R I E T L A E
N D K Q J X E I F B
O H I N D W E F U E
C G N K O Y T A Q C
D H S I A X H X T R
B H A R P S W E L L
```

39 MARYLAND CITIES

```
F R U I T L A N D G
F B A L T I M O R E
R O N L A U R E L K
E F N C S L B D U O
D T A N E Y T O W N
E X P J P M O U N T
R R O C K V I L L E
I V L U J V I N L E
C R I S F I E L D M
K D S R H B O W I E
```

40 MARYLAND LANDMARKS

```
D W Y E Y U W G A S
P X B L K Y X E I I
O B O L L M A N D O
H Z N I E D G A R N
A G T C R O W W P Y
M U N O M D U D K B
M O N T P E L I E R
O A N T I E T A M I
N K J G B P A D R C
D Q G T T U L I P E
```

41 MASSACHUSETTS CITIES

```
M E D F O R D F A Y
W X L M B M B R C V
O B N V E E C A H H
R V J K V L E M E O
C H A V E R H I L L
E Q Y T R O T N S Y
S O I A L S M G E O
T P K K Y E I H A K
E B O S T O N A V E
R Q U I N C Y M R S
```

42 MASSACHUSETTS LANDMARKS

```
G R G O D D A R D V
R B E A U P O R T E
O W A Z G L B C B T
P N N W E Y O W R E
I F U L L M A R A R
U E S D M O R Y N A
S N S T W U D J T N
S W S X O T M A W S
K A T M O H A W K F
F Y Z R D E N W P Z
```

13 — MICHIGAN CITIES

```
A  B  R  O  N  S  O  N  B  D
K  A  L  A  M  A  Z  O  O  E
A  A  H  D  W  B  U  R  C  A
D  B  A  L  L  D  F  B  L  R
E  M  R  T  A  F  R  W  A  B
T  T  R  U  P  N  A  T  W  O
R  E  I  S  E  M  S  J  S  R
O  S  S  Q  E  W  E  I  O  N
I  J  O  L  R  X  R  W  N  Q
T  Q  N  B  E  L  D  I  N  G
```

14 — MICHIGAN LANDMARKS

```
M  A  T  T  H  A  E  I  M  Z
B  C  R  A  N  B  R  O  O  K
C  E  D  I  S  O  N  H  T  U
A  P  A  B  R  I  E  I  O  W
L  E  V  V  B  I  S  G  W  T
U  W  J  J  B  U  T  H  N  S
M  A  R  S  H  A  L  L  I  E
E  B  G  Q  V  W  G  A  Y  Z
T  I  M  A  C  K  I  N  A  C
W  C  D  I  Q  J  Q  D  C  T
```

15 — MINNESOTA CITIES

```
M  R  P  L  Y  M  O  U  T  H
E  S  A  R  T  E  L  L  M  R
I  W  O  O  D  B  U  R  Y  O
P  A  N  C  M  E  D  W  I  S
B  U  J  H  B  D  U  L  Q  E
L  A  K  E  V  I  L  L  E  V
A  I  C  S  G  N  U  J  F  I
I  D  V  T  H  A  T  P  K  L
N  W  E  E  A  L  H  R  I  L
E  R  D  R  E  A  G  A  N  E
```

16 — MINNESOTA LANDMARKS

```
S  S  S  O  U  D  A  N  E  D
M  P  I  L  L  S  B  U  R  Y
A  U  Q  N  Y  D  Q  V  L  W
Y  Z  N  H  C  K  I  H  C  A
O  S  N  E  L  L  I  N  G  S
R  A  B  I  D  E  A  U  H  H
U  C  P  Z  O  K  B  I  C  B
K  E  L  L  O  G  G  W  R  U
J  Z  E  K  A  T  H  I  O  R
M  T  H  O  R  S  T  E  I  N
```

17 — MISSISSIPPI CITIES

```
H  B  C  S  T  F  I  L  P  G
T  B  W  O  A  U  T  B  E  U
U  I  U  U  H  S  P  L  A  L
U  L  U  T  H  E  A  E  R  P
L  O  Z  H  Q  K  W  Y  L  P
A  X  J  A  C  K  S  O  N  O
U  I  M  V  F  Q  I  F  B  R
R  U  L  E  L  A  N  D  J  T
E  O  B  N  M  O  R  T  O  N
L  R  I  D  G  E  L  A  N  D
```

18 — MISSISSIPPI LANDMARKS

```
L  O  N  G  W  O  O  D  L  W
O  D  E  N  T  Z  E  L  W  I
B  U  W  C  J  Q  J  R  A  N
E  N  Y  H  U  F  O  O  V  D
A  L  M  E  L  R  O  S  E  S
U  E  W  S  G  Z  N  A  R  O
V  I  P  T  S  O  E  L  L  R
O  T  T  E  Q  W  I  I  E  D
I  H  B  R  F  W  E  E  Y  Y
R  M  M  O  N  M  O  U  T  H
```

49 MISSOURI CITIES

```
F  P  L  I  B  E  R  T  Y  W
L  Q  J  O  P  L  I  N  B  B
O  I  X  G  U  B  Q  R  E  B
R  N  I  X  A  G  J  A  L  E
I  K  O  F  B  J  I  Y  T  U
S  L  I  X  T  U  D  T  O  R
S  G  L  A  D  S  T  O  N  E
A  M  O  N  E  T  T  W  E  K
N  O  G  Q  K  X  L  N  V  A
T  C  W  I  L  D  W  O  O  D
```

50 MISSOURI LANDMARKS

```
R  F  G  A  T  E  W  A  Y  M
O  B  O  T  A  N  I  C  A  L
H  S  P  D  B  X  C  S  W  A
L  P  A  Q  D  V  U  O  A  N
R  Q  F  G  H  M  C  N  T  H
P  E  S  Z  E  C  T  J  K  E
S  A  N  B  O  R  N  H  I  U
J  D  T  J  O  P  L  I  N  S
C  S  Z  E  H  O  Z  U  S  E
G  O  L  D  E  N  R  O  D  R
```

51 MONTANA CITIES

```
F  C  H  B  H  E  G  Q  B  P
V  E  O  E  L  C  S  O  O  L
X  N  M  L  L  M  Z  C  Z  E
R  E  I  G  S  E  S  H  E  N
R  P  S  R  P  T  N  S  M  T
O  N  S  A  O  F  R  A  A  Y
A  P  O  D  X  F  Z  I  N  W
N  L  U  E  H  O  O  O  P  O
K  A  L  I  S  P  E  L  L  O
W  R  A  S  I  D  N  E  Y  D
```

52 MONTANA LANDMARKS

```
T  R  A  V  E  L  E  R  S  R
S  O  J  N  Q  U  P  P  U  O
P  T  B  B  E  N  T  O  N  S
O  R  A  N  K  I  N  R  K  E
M  Q  N  D  H  J  F  T  N  B
P  E  N  Z  Z  A  T  A  X  U
E  F  A  Y  W  R  G  G  U  D
Y  B  C  Z  C  F  B  E  H  G
S  K  K  B  U  R  T  O  N  B
P  I  C  T  O  G  R  A  P  H
```

53 NEBRASKA CITIES

```
Q  I  C  B  V  X  N  X  J  X
U  G  V  L  I  N  C  O  L  N
S  E  W  A  R  D  R  P  B  L
N  C  G  I  J  K  A  T  E  K
O  L  E  R  A  L  L  M  A  E
R  W  N  A  E  E  S  R  T  A
F  R  E  M  O  N  T  N  R  R
O  D  V  S  W  Z  O  F  I  N
L  S  A  B  Q  U  N  M  C  E
K  M  J  O  M  A  H  A  E  Y
```

51 NEBRASKA LANDMARKS

```
C  A  C  W  A  L  K  E  R  Q
H  T  R  O  B  I  D  O  U  X
I  K  C  O  U  F  A  L  R  C
M  I  C  D  Z  Z  D  H  O  D
N  N  Q  Q  H  W  Q  A  B  A
E  S  C  H  U  L  T  Z  I  E
Y  O  Z  P  X  E  Z  A  N  C
B  N  J  I  G  A  O  R  S  M
P  A  L  M  E  R  Y  D  O  I
H  H  R  E  S  Y  W  D  N  A
```

55 NEVADA CITIES

```
Z C R C S P A R K S
H M R V W E L L S Y
E D N E Q B L M F C
N F E R N L E Y C A
D P L R Y O L X W R
E S K F A L L O N L
R I O Z C S M Z O I
S M E S Q U I T E N
O F N H T K Q Y P P
N T Q X G B T P S A
```

56 NEVADA LANDMARKS

```
V C F R A N C I S G
C H U R C H I L L R
I E T R K I M I K A
U C H A R C O A L I
H L E O N A R D F L
O P K R Z E M U U W
O L Y D O I O B B A
V O P O B U N A R Y
E W L O V E L O C K
R S T O K E S S V K
```

57 NEW HAMPSHIRE CITIES

```
G P D O V E R L C M
R O C H E S T E R A
U R W Q N U G B K N
S T K E E N E A N C
T S B E R L I N A H
R M E U R Z R O S F
C O N C O R D N H S
E U A Y V K K E U T
P T X T Q E T U A E
V H L A C O N I A R
```

58 NEW HAMPSHIRE LANDMARKS

```
J W E N T W O R T H
G O I L A D D A H Y
S R S E L X O U K M
U O C I B E Z G X S
L B A J A T Z U C Q
L E R J C H N S C J
I R T H O R N T O N
V T S C R M O U N T
A D F X E X Z S V N
N M W E B S T E R V
```

59 NEW JERSEY CITIES

```
P E L I Z A B E T H
A B E C L E C M Q C
T A X X L I O M Y A
E Y N O A I N C D M
R O E U N K F D D D
S N W D B E W T E E
O N A T R E N T O N
N E R H O B O K E N
C C K V D Y L Y J B
P L A I N F I E L D
```

60 NEW JERSEY LANDMARKS

```
S E A B R I G H T P
G M X O J Q C U C R
B A N A S S A U K I
O Y P M A T M D B N
X B D N N Z P O O C
W U R A D B U R N E
O R E V Y A H V C T
O Y X A O Q J E W O
D O C E M O R V E N
G R I N G W O O D I
```

61. NEW MEXICO CITIES

```
L O R D S B U R G G
M P E U N I C E R A
F O W J J C I F O M
D R C L O V I S S O
T T J Q A G W I W R
R A T O N R U H E I
K L E S P A N O L A
I E V J W N K B L R
C S H M D T H B T T
S O Y O F S K S T Y
```

62. NEW MEXICO LANDMARKS

```
R W X U J Y C P T M
B A N D E L I E R A
C G C S W K F C Y N
A O R O R K O O A U
R N Q L M U L S B E
L O Q B Y A S P L L
S A N D I A O C M I
B P U R B L M Q A T
A M E S I L L A H O
D E G L O R I E T A
```

63. NEW YORK CITIES

```
A A H B A T A V I A
Q S Y R A C U S E M
A N O R W I C H K S
B L I T F S O D I T
U P B T P H H O N E
F T W A F H O G G R
F Y Y O N K E R S D
A T Q M Q Y S W T A
L K H O E T A J O M
O L C H U D S O N C
```

64. NEW YORK LANDMARKS

```
C C J S K N G P X T
H L U H V I N R L B
R E B C X A S B E G
I R V G R G N S W E
S M A N H A T T A N
T O X J F R I E R E
E N K X X A F L O S
E T S K R O S C O E
N B O U G H T O N O
C M H H A R M O N Y
```

65. NORTH CAROLINA CITIES

```
E Y P R S V G M S S
H C T A L J A E H A
I O V L I D S W E L
C N Y E U O T X L I
K C W I L S O N B S
O O J G T T N F Y B
R R I H R C I Z B U
Y D D U R H A M N R
C H A R L O T T E Y
W K I N S T O N D K
```

66. NORTH CAROLINA LANDMARKS

```
H A Y E S C C X B C
Q S U P L K H T Z O
F G U I L F O R D O
C Q Z N O J W Y Y L
S A L E M X A O D M
A W P H L E N N G O
Z O C U P O L A L R
K H A R D A W A Y E
D V H S L A F C C K
G D V T T A V E R N
```

NORTH DAKOTA CITIES

NORTH DAKOTA LANDMARKS

OHIO CITIES

OHIO LANDMARKS

OKLAHOMA CITIES

OKLAHOMA LANDMARKS

73 OREGON CITIES

```
K  S  C  A  N  B  Y  P  N  S
E  C  J  U  T  F  R  O  M  A
I  A  N  E  W  P  O  R  T  L
Z  P  Z  T  U  G  W  T  T  E
E  P  Q  E  W  G  V  L  A  M
R  O  O  A  T  W  E  A  A  L
X  O  A  S  H  L  A  N  D  W
A  S  T  O  R  I  A  D  E  N
I  E  F  V  Q  A  X  F  N  P
P  E  N  D  L  E  T  O  N  L
```

74 OREGON LANDMARKS

```
W  O  P  T  U  P  V  L  K  T
A  S  T  O  R  I  A  I  G  I
L  M  I  J  C  T  Q  G  S  M
L  A  L  M  V  T  E  H  U  B
O  R  L  Y  A  O  P  T  N  E
W  I  A  G  S  C  K  S  K  R
A  T  M  A  O  K  M  H  E  L
P  I  O  N  E  E  R  I  N  I
M  M  O  B  X  E  T  P  M  N
U  E  K  L  A  M  A  T  H  E
```

75 PENNSYLVANIA CITIES

```
N  H  J  W  A  R  R  E  N  A
F  A  R  E  A  D  I  N  G  D
P  R  G  W  S  C  C  K  W  Y
I  R  V  G  H  O  X  T  T  T
T  I  J  L  A  E  E  R  A  V
T  S  O  T  R  S  T  R  R  M
S  B  Q  C  O  T  W  M  M  Y
T  U  C  K  N  E  R  I  E  N
O  R  O  Y  O  R  K  Z  O  S
N  G  S  C  R  A  N  T  O  N
```

76 PENNSYLVANIA LANDMARKS

```
C  W  B  P  U  L  P  I  T  R
E  B  C  O  A  Y  H  L  W  L
D  H  A  U  S  Z  H  Z  H  D
A  G  R  E  Y  T  A  S  A  A
R  I  R  H  A  S  Q  T  R  C
C  F  I  E  P  H  R  A  T  A
R  F  E  M  W  M  E  P  O  X
O  O  M  L  O  P  B  L  N  S
F  R  O  I  G  Q  P  E  P  T
T  D  I  V  U  B  E  T  H  D
```

77 RHODE ISLAND CITIES

```
K  A  W  A  R  W  I  C  K  E
F  C  C  Q  T  Q  M  D  J  X
P  R  O  V  I  D  E  N  C  E
G  A  V  U  V  I  B  F  N  T
W  N  E  K  E  F  R  I  E  E
H  S  N  K  R  O  I  Q  W  R
F  T  T  K  T  S  S  V  P  O
E  O  R  Q  O  T  T  N  O  Z
L  N  Y  L  N  E  O  P  R  J
W  E  S  T  E  R  L  Y  T  C
```

78 RHODE ISLAND LANDMARKS

```
F  A  K  O  G  F  J  B  M  J
X  L  I  Q  I  F  R  A  A  S
F  D  N  S  L  A  T  E  R  R
G  R  G  M  B  L  U  N  B  E
V  I  S  T  E  C  Q  X  L  D
E  C  C  U  R  H  N  T  E  W
R  H  O  J  T  O  W  B  D  O
N  D  T  H  U  N  T  E  R  O
O  B  E  L  L  E  V  U  E  D
N  H  C  R  E  S  C  E  N  T
```

79 SOUTH CAROLINA CITIES

```
V E C F J G Y G A G
C A Y C E X R R I K
S S A L Q C L E K R
U L N I Y O V E E A
M E D N D L I N N R
T Y E T L U H V Z M
E U R O O M N I F E
R A S N L B Y L L Y
M F O J I I J L B I
H A N A H A N E I G
```

80 SOUTH CAROLINA LANDMARKS

```
F M I L L F O R D V
L E H Z Z Q O R H E
X P I D B H K I O M
N E B O R O U G H A
X A E T O T Y U F N
W C R E B S W C P U
V H N U I N D X E E
P O I N S E T T N L
D I A Z A E X O N W
C D N P O M P I O N
```

81 SOUTH DAKOTA CITIES

```
B R A N D O N R K Q
W R T V W A R N E R
V O L G A H W H N M
B H H G T I U D J I
I L P I E R R E J L
S P E A R F I S H B
F P S K T J K E V A
T H U R O N R Q B N
E H X H W G O N O K
A F L A N D R E A U
```

82 SOUTH DAKOTA LANDMARKS

```
D E A D W O O D V N
R Y M W O U N D E D
U P I E R R E Z R I
S J N F R A W L E Y
H D U D R U B K N F
M I I C H E L L D I
O Z E A K Z O Q R I
R Q M T L Q O U Y C
E D A E M F M X E C
O R N M O L S T A D
```

83 TENNESSEE CITIES

```
B A R T L E T T P W
J K F G A Z L K P E
Z I R V P Y X L B M
Z N A S H V I L L E
R G N L L P I A M M
C S K G O Q F L A P
R P L F J U Z G R H
U O I I B O D O T I
M R N G T M X O I S
P T C O W A N D N I
```

84 TENNESSEE LANDMARKS

```
F R A N K L I N D W
M X C B R Y M A N Y
A E D R L M D B Q N
S Y C A M O R E O N
O O Y T X C U R P E
N T G T L C I N C W
I U Z L T A Z R T O
C J S E M S Z G X O
X U J U B I L E E D
P I N S O N T H S L
```

85 — TEXAS CITIES

```
F R E E R Q O S H H
L P C P O B P Y O A
Y H E L O T E S U R
D U L J A D G J S L
E D I N B U R G T I
F N N G P B S R O N
E A A I P L L T N G
W I T I J I X K I E
J E T E S N R K M N
S F L U B B O C K S
```

86 — TEXAS LANDMARKS

```
H V E C B U W L X O
A H J O H D Z R P Q
R L A N D E R G I N
R U C C A A D B D E
E D I H J L X R D S
L C N O M E A O X P
L P T C L Y T M T A
F P O K D H R A O D
F R A N D O L P H A
S P I N D L E T O P
```

87 — UTAH CITIES

```
N K A Y S V I L L E
D E M L M D L A F B
H N I J O R O Y F O
T I L R R O A T E U
P B L P O Z E O V N
P L C K N N P N P T
H E R R I M A N R I
X Y E S J L P T O F
R A E J W A M Q V U
X I K D E L T A O L
```

88 — UTAH LANDMARKS

```
U K G S H Q R W G H
X R U B I N G H A M
D E S O L A T I O N
O E B Q U A R R Y Z
U D R W C L D Q D R
G O I C D K A S E M
L P G O C A N Y O N
A S H A A L G E I K
S T A P F I E E G D
J X M X V B R Y C E
```

89 — VERMONT CITIES

```
H H X X M F B P B W
M I L T O N S O A I
S S T T N I W W R N
H L L C T T A N T O
E L D A P H N A O O
L G P S E I T L N S
D G U I L F O R D K
O W V N I S N N T I
N F S X E B A R R E
L J H A R T L A N D
```

90 — VERMONT LANDMARKS

```
S O C I A L I S T X
T N M O U N T N B C
E J A A W Q D Y M Q
L U D U P I H P P M
L S H E L B U R N E
A T A M C A L V I N
F I M M H E K U H B
A N W A W S U H P D
N V R O B E R T A
E G M C R O K E B Y
```

91 VIRGINIA CITIES

```
F Y S G A L A X U R
A L T O G N O G R I
I S A L E M E M A C
R S U F F O L K D H
F H N S N D T Z F M
A J T N L O C T O O
X S O H U T R P R N
E V N D Y K K T D D
T N U H A M P T O N
L E E S B U R G Z N
```

92 VIRGINIA LANDMARKS

```
M O N T I C E L L O
C W I K Y W S H M M
P W T O O Y H O R A
E D G A R T I Y I N
Q Y Y I K H R Q P A
D Q K Z T E L E S S
K E N M O R E R H S
Y R A D W E Y H I A
A R L I N G T O N S
Z S T O N E W A L L
```

93 WASHINGTON CITIES

```
V A N C O U V E R R
U K O L Y M P I A R
E W E N A T C H E E
S D V N T S R Q W N
E A E Q T D L K D T
A B R U B V G W U O
I B E L L E V U E N
T A T A C O M A G S
L U T F Z Z Q K G O
E S P O K A N E P Z
```

94 WASHINGTON LANDMARKS

```
Z N T O W N S E N D
K I Z W O R D E N P
K S E H C X I F U A
P Q F W H I T M A N
I U I M I W P M I A
U A B E N E W A H M
N L O U O N X R N A
E L A U O M H M P Z
E Y R E K F O E R U
R E A C T O R S J Z
```

95 WEST VIRGINIA CITIES

```
M O R G A N T O W N
L O G A N C E J H B
A W U S W F L X E W
P E W B E C K L E Y
H I N T O N I U L I
E R V I E N N A I E
T T E K X R S A N M
L O S D X D J J G Y
O N P H I L I P P I
C H A R L E S T O N
```

96 WEST VIRGINIA LANDMARKS

```
S C L O V E R B G A
E A Q L W V Y Z R W
Y M L B E F C V E C
C P Q H S J S F E L
R B M A T E W A N Y
E E G G O L V P B U
E L B P N K N U R V
K L J E V I E F I A
Q U C A R N I F E X
V D A V I S T K R E
```

97 WISCONSIN CITIES

```
Y  K  W  X  G  B  M  X  M  Q
B  E  L  O  I  T  E  L  E  N
L  N  B  B  A  R  R  O  N  F
F  O  L  Y  P  P  R  W  O  M
L  S  A  P  P  V  I  C  M  A
I  H  D  R  L  R  L  G  O  D
J  A  J  L  E  T  L  S  N  I
E  C  H  E  T  E  K  X  I  S
O  S  H  K  O  S  H  Q  E  O
R  A  C  I  N  E  M  L  T  N
```

98 WISCONSIN LANDMARKS

```
T  A  L  I  E  S  I  N  O  A
M  F  E  R  M  R  V  T  C  Z
I  J  T  I  M  I  I  C  O  T
L  K  U  S  E  L  L  I  N  A
W  G  R  A  I  W  L  T  T  L
A  O  N  C  S  X  A  F  O  A
U  J  E  U  N  T  N  B  T  N
K  B  R  I  S  B  O  I  S  U
E  P  V  M  I  G  I  R  X  Z
E  G  P  D  O  U  S  M  A  N
```

99 WYOMING CITIES

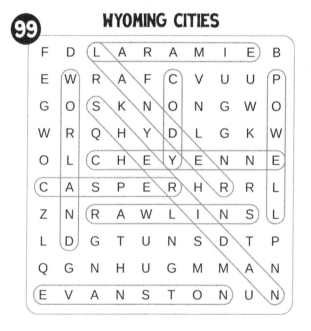

```
F  D  L  A  R  A  M  I  E  B
E  W  R  A  F  C  V  U  U  P
G  O  S  K  N  O  N  G  W  O
W  R  Q  H  Y  D  L  G  K  W
O  L  C  H  E  Y  E  N  N  E
C  A  S  P  E  R  H  R  R  L
Z  N  R  A  W  L  I  N  S  L
L  D  G  T  U  N  S  D  T  P
Q  G  N  H  U  G  M  M  A  N
E  V  A  N  S  T  O  N  U  N
```

100 WYOMING LANDMARKS

```
N  J  U  M  Z  L  W  L  T  G
F  Q  B  U  D  B  A  R  I  U
M  A  V  R  V  T  P  B  X  E
Z  H  M  I  T  N  I  A  H  R
E  X  P  E  D  I  T  I  O  N
B  T  S  O  S  C  I  P  R  S
W  O  B  S  I  D  I  A  N  E
I  M  M  L  V  T  S  U  E  Y
J  A  C  K  S  O  N  T  R  O
E  O  X  L  A  R  A  M  I  E
```

FREE BONUS

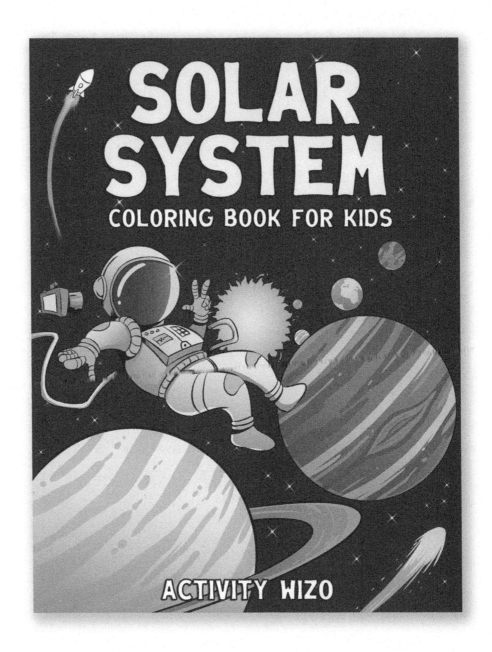

Get This FREE Bonus Now!

Just go to: activitywizo.com/free

THANK YOU!

Made in United States
North Haven, CT
12 February 2022

16050985R00070